THE BRIDPORT

POETRY, SHORT STORIES AN

JUDGES
Patience Agbabi • Poetry
Tessa Hadley • Short Stories
Tim Stevenson • Flash Fiction

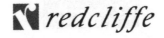

First published in 2016 by Redcliffe Press Ltd
81g Pembroke Road, Bristol BS8 3EA

e: info@redcliffepress.co.uk
www.redcliffepress.co.uk
Follow us on Twitter @RedcliffePress

Follow The Bridport Prize:
Follow us on Twitter @BridportPrize
www.bridportprize.org.uk
www.facebook.com/bridportprize

ISBN 978-1-911408-03-1

British Library Cataloguing-in-Publication Data
A catalogue record for this book is available from the British Library

Typeset in 10.5pt Times

Typeset by Addison Print Ltd, Northampton
Printed by Hobbs the Printers Ltd, Totton

Contents

PATIENCE AGBABI

Poetry Report

I asked for poems with a pulse, eliciting a visceral response; poems with a sense of urgency; poems unfettered by the autobiographical, fired by the imagination; poems taking risks in form, content or idea; multilayered poems echoing long after they were read.

And I got what I wished for: 200 poems, all with some merit. Even poems I quickly discarded felt like gifts. The judging was more pleasurable than I imagined which made me wonder about the overall standard of the entries I didn't see.

As in recent years, most poems were free verse, but there were a surprising number of 14-liners, some of them sonnets; some used regular metre or effective repetition which was very welcome. Others rhymed arbitrarily or had erratic line breaks: I wished they'd been read aloud before submission. There were lots of poems about death or loss, some transcending the personal, using form to focus the grief; equally moving poems about sexism, autism. Nature was popular but no eco-poetry. Too many poems seemed autobiographical, fettered by strict adherence to fact. I wanted more creativity. But there were enough playful or dark imaginative poems to whet my appetite. Quite a few poems about sex, possibly inspired by my call to take risks in content. Far fewer took risks with an idea: the ones that did so successfully stood out.

The judging process coincided fortuitously with the Rio Olympics. On summer holiday at home, I'd read an hour's worth of poems every morning before joining the family. This mental workout was a great way to start the day. Watching a range of sports, from synchronised diving to athletics, heightened my response to the technical side of poetry. It reminded me how much work goes into a great poem for it to appear effortless as a flawless gymnastic routine. More than anything, it confirmed what I felt to be the case for the majority of the longlisted poems: they needed more work. Many began well but dipped in the middle or end, where the language became prosaic or lapsed into cliché. The spell was broken. The poet had not yet honed their technical skills, ran out of time, or lacked stamina. Maybe they didn't understand the fundamentals of punctuation or struggled with line endings and stanza breaks so had erratic control over the pace. Or they weren't obsessive enough about achieving perfection.

I also assessed level of difficulty, whether the poem was playing safe or ambitious. You can only take a risk when you know what you're doing i.e. know the rules before you break them. And ask yourself *Why is this a poem?* Why is poetry the best form for this material? What can poetry do that prose can't? The best poems were masters of the form. They understood sound and image: how to use white space.

Technicalities aside, there's a gut reaction at play during the judging process. With some poems, it's love at first sight whereas others grow on you. My 'maybe' pile was high. I wanted to give these poems an extra chance to work their magic, rereading them many times. I take the visceral response very seriously indeed. If a poem was still haunting me at the end of that fortnight, it was likely to make the anthology.

I give first prize to 'Spitting Distance'. It has a directness, an understated authority of voice: *So this is what it's like to be a gun.* There's tension in its couplets, it knows when to use enjambment and when not. It rhymes irregularly so you barely notice yet this punctuates the voice, enhances the pleasure. The images are tangible: the path *falling like a braid*, a chimney *hangs from the sky/on a white string*. Finally, the poem takes a bold risk at the end and manages to carry it off. This is poetry at its best.

Second prize goes to 'Chickens', set in a Florida classroom where the teacher gives a lesson on 'conditioned behaviour'. The fluid, filmic couplets are irregularly interrupted by the sound of a yardstick being hit against a lectern. Each *thwack* catapults the reader into a different character and timezone with exceptional skill. The poem continues to surprise and astound me with each rereading.

'Silk' takes the third prize. From its latent feminist opening: *For those weeks the houses belonged to/the women* to the end, it sustains a single sentence over 24 lines, a narrative thread as finely wrought as the silk itself. All five senses are put on hold in the earlier stanzas as the houses are prepared for the silkworms: the poem builds, layer upon layer of detail; then in the final stanza, smell, taste and touch explode, the syntax ensuring a poetic climax at the very last word.

Congratulations to the winners, the Highly Commended and all those who made the longlist. Your work has reminded me how vital poetry is to our existence, how it shapes our response to the world and has a living, breathing pulse.

TESSA HADLEY

Short Story Report

My reading each time begins sceptically. Stepping into a short story, I'm always resisting it until it wins me over. First of all, it wins me over through its sentences, because they're not cliched, because they're musical and they're exact. I can see what they're describing, I can grasp their thought, I know where I am. The best writing is so deliciously plain and clear: as in these beginnings, for example. 'A trellis separates the patio behind Elizabeth's house from the door to the rooms where the servants live' ('Moore's Alley'), or '"Watch this," Lateef says and he reaches under the goat and starts pulling and squeezing' ('Lateef's Room'). The detail is precise and vivid, the vocabulary isn't fussy, there's a scrupulous concern to denote exactly what's required for the story to get started and for the reader to be carried inside it, involved and interested, sensuously present.

Of course I'm talking about good style here, and what I'm saying applies as much to writing novels as short stories. Everything in a good sentence should feel original, but not strained or effortful. (I know – so much effort goes into it. Only it mustn't show.) Sometimes a sentence has something extraordinary or miraculous in it: but that too should be exact – the miraculous should feel hard-won, as if a great deal of solidity, of real building-work, has earned the writer their moment of letting go. There's a gorgeous letting go at the end of 'Uncle Frank's Turkeys', when the farmer is feeding his turkeys. 'He bends down to the sack and throws handfuls in big arcs. The grain floats in a shining circle for a moment, and then sinks back down in slow motion to the waiting turkeys.' In 'The Disappeared Girl', in the middle of real country life and hard work, there's a bit of magic. 'There was a slit in the bark of that tree, just big enough for a girl to slip through. It was cool inside, green moss, soft and cushioney. She lay down, just a minute. Nobody's laid eyes on her since.'

Another thing good sentences can do is catch the right idiom of a world, capture its flavour for us. In 'Brylcreem Boy' Jim Waite remembers a girl's petticoat in 1960: 'yards and yards of stiff material that made the lower half of her dress stick out like a ripe lettuce, ballooning over my lap'. In 'The War Against The Monsters' we can vividly hear the voice of awful, haunted Auntie Brenda, with her appetite for horrors. 'Hours he were stuck – that suicide. Up to his neck in clinging mud. And then he came to – and do you know what he saw?' Some good writers just have this gift for mimicry, this 'good ear' – others don't, it's not their thing. But it's a lovely asset if you do have it.

A story shouldn't read like an extract from a novel, or a compressed novel, with just too much crammed into its short space. A good short story has a satisfying single-mindedness, it drives purposefully and economically towards its ending, you can hold it in your mind all at once. 'Avalanche' is so shapely and dramatically effective: four friends are caught up in an avalanche and the terrible drama of their rescue clarifies and simplifies the messy sprawl of the relationships. In 'Bonxie' a woman has retreated to the Orkneys to write her novel, then finds herself in a tragi-comic confrontation with a huge seabird trapped in her bathroom. The single story-element encapsulates a much larger complexity and irony.

Endings are the hardest thing to get right in a short story. At the end of 'Expiating Irene' a daughter with her eyes closed listens to her mother reminiscing and fibbing and singing. And a tender moment in 'Porn Star Names' might have been too sweet, if Jo Holmwood hadn't finished on a different beat, by returning to the boys' funny sex fascination.

My three finalists have all achieved just the right poised, liberating, exhilarating closure to their stories. All these three stories are so completely different! I didn't plan for that, but it makes a nice point. 'Steroid Dreams' is just so beautifully written, every sentence poised and funny and intelligent. The prose has a marvellous rhythm, rich with perceptions. 'Open House' is much stranger. Who knows whether that bear in the garden is real, or some phantom expression of the wildness in this odd family? The crazy party and its aftermath of wreckage are superbly done, so enigmatic and terrifying and exhilarating. And 'Cut Loose'! It seems to be written in a single perfect breath, so apparently artless yet perfectly controlled. There's simply nothing out of place in this hushed, tensed imagining of the twisted history of violence between a man and a woman, all wrapped up as austerely as a Greek drama inside one lonely room, in a few short weeks of waiting.

TIM STEVENSON

Flash Fiction Report

The difficulty with judging any flash-fiction competition is simply the astonishing variety of the work submitted. Some competitions have themes to narrow the horizon of artistic vision, but when faced with such an accomplished group of stories, that vary quite spectacularly within the parameters of the spectrum, there is nothing for it but to grab your sharpest pencil, brew a really hot cup of tea, and settle down to a good read.

This year, as in every year at the Bridport, the quality is high. It is a pleasure to read such accomplished works but, on the other hand, it makes it all the harder to slide a razor between them. There have been car accidents and the subtleties of loss, the loveless moments that come from the premature ownership of false teeth, the horrific choices of hard times, and many others that sprang from the page and ended up, quite rightly, on the shortlist.

Which brings me neatly onto the subject of the final three.

This year, when asked what I was looking for in a flash-fiction, I gave the same reply I give to anyone who wants to know what, in my opinion, really makes a flash work. My thoughts are that a reader must have a clear sense of what happened before the story began; a frame into which these new events can be placed. Secondly, a sense of time; a deep awareness that events are unfolding at exactly the right pace for the story being told – sometimes fast, sometimes slow, but always measured. Thirdly, the end of the story must lead the reader into the future, giving enough information to extrapolate what comes next, and what that might mean for the characters involved.

Irrespective of the subject, this is what I look for, and try my hardest to write, for that matter.

The three winners for this year's competition each fulfil these criteria to a tee.

'467 Strathmore Ave.' gives us memory and loss, and the ache of time passing as a distant tragedy fades; people get on with their lives and fall into 'their own private calamities' as the only true guardians of that fateful day are the flinching dogs.

The next, 'Dentures', is a sidelong commentary on the fickle nature of people who cannot see beyond mere physical beauty; who see their own youth reflected in the bodies of others, the outcomes that might have been if only different choices had been made and, finally, the searing practicality of a mother's love.

The last, 'Drought', is a quiet masterclass in detail and understatement; an observation of time through changes in a landscape that bind together a mother and child. The mother herself becomes a child through memories invoked by new, once-familiar landmarks that have been transformed by the flood. 'There are sunken places, so the tales say...' is the herald, the gap between a grandmother's knee and the future for the young girl, unbound from an ancestral home and all the obligations that go with it. She will write new stories, tell new tales from after the flood, and weave a new mythology for her children and all those who come after.

In this story, more than any other this year, I could clearly see the ripples in time, both backwards and forwards, that are framed by a story far smaller than the ripples themselves, but a story that is still able to contain enough truth and meaning to see clearly where the flow of time will take us.

It has been a pleasure to read the entries this year; I predict that those authors still unpublished will not have too long to wait before success becomes a well-deserved reality.

Congratulations to you all, each piece was a delight. I'm just sorry I had to choose.

MARK PAJAK

Spitting Distance

Near Edale, I find a live rifle shell
like a gold seed in the earth.

So I load it into my mouth
and go on walking, the sun

breathing down my neck,
the head of Mam Tor rising

and the path falling like a braid.
So this is what it's like to be a gun;

copper bleeding on the gums,
the domino click in the teeth.

At the blue summit, I look down
with my new perspective

on the warped floor of Derbyshire,
to where a village pools in a valley

and a chimney hangs from the sky
on a white string. And I watch

with hunger the red dot of a car
stop at a crossroads. I suck hard

on the blunt bud, drawing out
its deeper flavour of powder,

smoke down the barrel
of my throat. Then it hits me

that there's another side to this.
And I lay in the warm heather.

A body with a bullet
in its head staring at this sky.

Its clouds blown open.
Its sudden night.

LAURA WATSON

Chickens

Speaking of conditioned behavior in a cold Florida classroom,
our teacher, who seemed always to have just finished a cigarette

and whose perfectly dentured mouth said *fangers* and *warsh,*
took, by way of example, the yardstick

from its dusty cradle that hung below the chalkboard,
and brought it, full force, flat side against the lectern.

The resulting *thwack* – pure, parochial – carried through the class.
It hit off the concrete block and the waxed tile floor,

off the air-conditioned tops of the science tables
where, the week before, a line of frogs

was pinned in flight before us. And more to his point,
it travelled over us, through us, our twelve year-old selves,

to the back of the lab, where it fell over the brood
of yellow-brown chicks warming themselves under the heat lamps

and pecking at the shit-upon newspaper that lined their temporary pen.
Each, and all at once, their soft bodies went still,

except in their stillness there was something
that made them sway: forward, backward, forward again

in a short, invisible arc, each a little pendulum
counting the time, until, one by one, the full dozen of them

recovered. Caroline, as willowy as her mother,
will find her stepfather in bed beside her. She snapped upright

in her chair, the heavy yellow curls of her hair
swinging to and fro in the inch above her shoulders.

Thwack. Heidi, at twenty-five, will violate
parole. She sat apart, in the first row, the first to see the yardstick

raised in the air, and the first to feel it move
a thin bar of air in front of her. She leaned into it –

the breeze and the backswing – before softening
in her chair. *Thwack*. Our teacher swung the yardstick

a fourth time, a fifth, the worn white oak of the lectern
giving up to the fluorescent air a veil of chalk dust,

almost a comet's tail, that split the room in two,
and as it settled, the chicks behind us paused and swayed

and began again their small activity. *Thwack*. Jessie,
in her quiet way, will swallow all the aspirin

she can find. *Thwack*. Brad will lose his brother. Jason, his dad.
Two of us will go to war and one of us will come back.

Thwack. The sun filtered through the chicken-wire windows
casting a wattled shadow on the opposite wall

and we sat in the full light of the classroom. *Thwack*.
And the chickens, by then, there was no pause in them at all.

CAROLINE PRICE

Silk

For those weeks the houses belonged to
the women, in April when sun had warmed the air
inside to a constant degree and the floors had been
swept scrupulously free of dust and debris
and they had laid out their simplest, cleanest
clothes to wear and stopped cooking with garlic

while the men stayed clear; later they would have
their role, knocking out pipes and keeping the dogs
away and the cockerel and chasing the fowls from the doors
so no sound or whiff of another creature might penetrate
to the rooms where the cages sat, criss-crossed
with supports, crammed with mulberry leaves

but for now they hung in the background and watched
as their wives moved slowly, serenely as queens
through the conferred distinction
of their houses, the cotton pouches of eggs tied beneath their clothes
bumping gently against breasts and thighs –
imagining the weight of those little bags

in their own hands as they waited, avid
for the moment of hatching, knowing so well
the voracious appetite that came after, the sickly-sweet
odour of saliva filling nostrils
and mouth and throat, the tenacious grown worm
drawing steadily out of itself its miracle.

SARAH BARR

Making Tea, Drinking Coffee

I suppose it can only be a good thing –
everyday activities that have become art.

Drinking tea, making coffee,
sex in its various positions.

Thinking carefully about what I'm doing
and thinking about what I am thinking.

Also, doing things very slowly.
We all have a chance to be artists.

Now – it's the art of tidying the house.
Find your socks,

pair them and roll them together,
then squash them upright in a drawer.

Soon, it might be putting the bins out
in a joyful way. Or, bathroom rituals.

Our quarrels and makings-up are a sort of art.
What you heard, what I said and why.

What I really meant and how you took it
and why you make your usual reply.

GLYNIS CHARLTON

Mirror Image

Tomorrow, he will take your breast,
the stranger in the mask and gown.
You'll look the same when you are dressed.

You joked you liked that one the best;
your way of coping – act the clown.
Tomorrow, he will take your breast.

They'll plump your pillows, *get some rest*,
then read your chart and write and frown.
You'll look the same when you are dressed.

They'll send it off. Another test,
this time without you. Don't look down.
Tomorrow, he will take your breast.

A year ago, you never guessed
at fear so deep that you could drown.
You'll look the same when you are dressed.

There'll be an ache where you once pressed
the part that let the whole side down.
Tomorrow, he will take your breast.
You'll look the same when you are dressed.

JENNY DANES

Notes on missing a person

This is his body   written for me
his chin will be the last to go   I know its beard
the way a child knows texture for the first time
top of his chest, yes, but I'm a little vague
about the nipples   stomach, backside, mouth most
definitely   I've lost the legs and hands, to forget his hands
how could I   I know his neck and his freckles
I remember noticing them for the first time
This is my body   it does not know what to do
it is learning what it means to be untouched
it is singing from the rocks   it has no trust in memory
and does not believe he was ever here   it is retreating
to belong only to itself   it is ordinary again
it cannot understand   the lack of him

ELIZABETH EZRA

The quiet, the breath

Two breaths in a room
With the curtains drawn

The quiet, the breath
The quiet, the breath

The baby, the child
Asleep in a room

In the warmth, in the night
The quiet, the breath

The baby, the child
Asleep in a room

The love and the love
The quiet, the breath

This is what stays
When all else is gone

The quiet, the breath
The quiet, the breath

The love and the love
The quiet, the breath

BEATRICE GARLAND

Yet another poem about the moon

Henri plants his tomatoes by the moon,
following the ebb and flow of that great orb,
its roughcast skin, its luminous high-voltage shine.

Everything that grows above the ground
needs sap to rise: so cabbages and beans and peas
he tucks in well before the moon grows round –

even one day past full and already it's too late.
But crops that burgeon underground are different.
Potatoes, beetroot, carrots, swedes, must wait

until the disc begins to shrink and fade, taking
the sap down into them for growth. Henri
looks us in the eye, his four-square figure reckoning

that we, urban, ignorant, science-fed,
will smile, or raise an eyebrow, but do just what he says,
while keeping doubts inside. Unsaid.

But when at midnight, the wide photograph
that's daily colour-printed by the sun
reverts to black and white, its negative,

it finds me sleepless, wild-eyed, half-undone –
and then I know he's right: that brilliant sphere,
the full moon rising, exerts her dark pull everywhere.

BEN JOHNSON

The Devotional

Having visited Scafden, I feel us at Pikeshill
are a different widowkind, not so moved
upon, more praiseful and less deeding.

This village supplied five bills and four bows,
all foot dragging their way war-ward.
We cold-a-bed now, husbands to ourself.

I read our stones every Sunday, the flowers
spray woodbined and cornflower, reveal
nothing. Still we steadfast, hymning beneath.

We all child left, some hands, others little
more than mouths, still voiceless, milk
hungry, mewling deep into moonlight.

Five days a week we straw split and plait.
Saturdays at dawn sharp we start bundling
marketward and haggle up to duskish.

But come May these hands will clasp Scafden
callous to Pikeshill callous and we young-girl-footed
will dance in showered sun, light as lambs.
One widowkind, ribbon weaving our ungreyed hair.

ANTHONY LAWRENCE

Scan

Even here, where medicine is nuclear
and assessment involves a risk of over-
exposure to winds that blow through you,

silently, you turn to love and hold her
memory under the slow revolve
of a ceiling so low, you can touch

the dead stars of rivets and lights that appear
along the runway and terminus of your bones.
The isotopic dye your blood has been

diverting to your extremities, leaves
an afterglow such as a ghost
that has enslaved your pulse and core

temperature might trail as it tours
your veins. And as you lie wired inside
a long machine that scans

the inner workings of your life
your skeleton illuminates a monitor
the clavicle and femur like details

from a satellite map
patched with intemperate weather.
Elsewhere, reading the graphic narrative

of your pain, a doctor
finds a crown of thorns starfish
where your spleen should be, and inside
the sprung cage of your ribs

a wounded animal bleeds
into the margins of your sleep.

A soft clipping calls time
on full body immersion, and when
you emerge, gowned and sliding

like a sea burial, a voice comes over
speakers set into the wall:
Please don't move, we're almost there,

which is what you believe you'd heard
behind a flashlight the night
they came through the roof to cut you

from the wreck. You look back
into a machine that is dark and silent
as the one you were in when

they lifted you away, your arms around
her waist, her eyes fixed on something
somewhere beyond the future.

Rwanda

The bar, 5pm. Green Mützig bottles
catch the sun, as District Leaders,
Policemen, Doctors, Moto-Drivers
observe the moves of two opponents.

With easy concentration, twinkling,
Executive cups a handful of marbles
and, working smartly around the board,
flips a marble into each bowl

until he runs out, then claims the heap
he lands upon, and starts again.
Each move is calculated to accumulate 'cows',
vigorous slaps or judicious applause,

clouding the muted discussions in corners
through the grey-blue smoke of cigarettes:
the whispered stratagems regarding taxations,
inheritance laws, cooperatives.

The marbles make little chinks against wood,
delicate, sequential, beaded sounds
chiming with the noise of bottles and cash,
the clinks of dreamy acquiescence

echoing the lilt of the stream outside
where children highlight the evening hours
with yellow jerry-cans, then balance back home,
accustomed bare feet on the dusted roads,

towards banana groves and shaded huts
where families, cross-legged, by the goats,
suck banana beer through bamboo
and dip fingers gently into the earth

to form precise bowl-shaped indentations
across the soft ground, and drop in pebbles
to play their version. It's just the same
except that the counters are soundless.

EILIS STANLEY

Crumbs and Conversation

At the dinner table he waits for the words to drop in.
It's taking longer; the clasp holding his wallet of gems
has broken en route to his seventies, and the sweets

of usage have scattered over a hundred-mile radius.
He'll never get round them, even if he leaves now
and takes a sneaky sabbatical from the conversation.

In between the cold cuts and nettle pesto, he starts to
compose ready made sentences, rolled out and shaped
to hold in his mind like a small, familiar, loved book.

His inner rehearsals hidden in the busy bounce
and tumble of table banter; the wit and words
that fall so lightly from the lips of others;

pearls of acuity that perform in the line of duty.
He trapezes out with an old anecdote, feeling the thrill
of attention, swinging high above the narrative; he chances

a small detour, only to slip hands with the main thread
and land in a soup of word croutons that won't soften,
but bob up and down on the story's surface.

A few wisps of watery laughter relieve him from repetition.
He bends to his soup and sips; a lone full stop
lost in the chatter and buttered rounds of garlic bread.

JEAN STEVENS

Skeleton

At the foot of Malham Cove
lost among stones and grass
through snow, wind and rain
the skeleton whitened

before a scorch of light
cast red, pink, yellow
returned flesh to skull, tibia, ulna
washed blood through veins.

The chest rose and fell
eyelids trembled

clothes flew back to the body.
He stood in the fell-runner's boots
he loved and the college outfit
his mother scrimped to buy.

Then he was up top again giddy
peering down the long, stony way
toes wavering over the edge
till he broke the trance
and slid his feet back, back,

back to the pedals on his bike
going widdershins down the lane
to the cottage and kitchen table
back to the simple choice
of what that day was for.

JOHN WHEELER

This Is My Gun

This is my gun.
Not many like it.
This one is mine.

Strange.
A thing both hard and soft.
Blued and silky and cool.
Rub your hand along the barrel, and it satisfies.

Almost magic.
Pull here...
things happen...
there.

Any movie tells the story.
Lose your gun and you're a nobody.
But I'm somebody.
Don't try to tell me I'm not.

Gun has one purpose.
Perfect and single.
Knife you can use to
cut a steak
whittle a stick
trim a rope...
Not a gun.
It's always waiting.
Aching to speak.
Be itself.

This is my gun.
Not many like it.
This one is mine.

So now.

Time to start.

WENDY BRANDMARK

Cut Loose

I drove all night not even stopping to eat till I reached Denver. Because when he figured I was really gone, not just hiding, he'd know where I was heading. I called Sharon when I hit town. I said if Richard comes you never heard.

She said why d'you go out there with him? You knew.

I had to find a hideaway life before he came searching. He would find me, he would not, would. Why I took that flat hidden behind a trailer house. A man in a wheelchair and his wife showed me out back to a dirt yard where it stood all alone: a two-storey wooden cabin, outside steps leading up to the apartment. Single bed, square wooden table. They'd put a candle on the table and the curtains I could see were hand sewn. They were trying, oh so desperate.

The man in the wheelchair waited while I descended with his wife who held on to the wooden rail for dear life. I could not say to his hollowed out face that the flat was terrible, a rickety room on stilts. He asked, 'You like it?' I imagined myself dead up there with them picking over me.

'I like it fine. Just I can't decide yet.'

He said, 'If you don't like it then you can go elsewhere.'

His wife frowned at him. How many people had even bothered to climb the stairs? 'You'll see. You won't find anything cheaper,' she said.

'Maybe,' I said looking around again at the dirt yard with not a spot of green, not even a weed. Richard would never think to look for me here. No one would. I'd disappear every time I entered the passage which led from the street past their house to the cabin.

So that evening having looked at apartments which faced the streets where Richard would walk, his face upturned, just looking for a glimpse of me, catching even my reflection in the window, I returned.

The man in the wheelchair was sitting in the yard. He said, 'you couldn't find anything better, could you?'

His wife said, 'I knew you would. You were the one.'

29

They were Henry and Estelle, and he'd got where he was falling down those stairs in what had been a hardware and timber yard. She made ends meet torch dancing in a club up on Colfax.

I hardly slept that first night. The cabin was so flimsy that it trembled with every truck rolling down the street. And whenever it stopped trembling, I heard little sounds, clicking as if there were birds in the room, and sometimes a whispering when the wind blew against the wooden walls. The slightest movement, my footsteps, even the door slamming shut in the trailer house, shook the floor. When I told Henry how it shook, he said, 'no way. That is built solid.'

In the morning I went job hunting. I knew not to search in my usual places, bars and cheap restaurants where Richard would look, leaning across the counter to ask if they had seen a troubled lady. Last time he posed as a devoted lover whose girl had gone missing. So good looking that the other waitress said to me, 'If you don't want him, just say.'

I remember a night when the crowd in the bar was like a bouquet of flowers, me in the center serving beers. And then his face appearing like a purple rose. His hand went over mine as I took money from a laughing woman buying for her boyfriend.

'Not here,' I said. He held my hand down till I agreed to come with him later. He said I could not cope without him. That I had been a street girl. Which was never true. I had lived in group houses where no one belonged to anyone else before he claimed me.

After we got together, I told him I might leave. He took both my hands and I saw that I could make him cry. Sometimes we stayed in our little room all day, Richard talking and talking about what was wrong with me and how he could fix me. When I said I wanted free he'd come inside me again. He knew my skin, hair, my breasts scrawny like the rest of me, as if they were his own.

I was lucky. An old age home needed someone to cook in the morning. Their girl had left a week ago. I had done some breakfast work for one of the cafés back in Boston, and I talked this up enough for them to hire me. It wasn't my kind of place, where old women moved around on canes or wheelchairs, everything slow and warm, me stirring their soupy porridge and ladling it into bowls. But I couldn't see Richard stepping into the little office here and asking the matron, a tough woman with curls like wire, if his lady had come knocking. I felt so safe I could sleep there and I did. When I finished the dishes from the morning run, I'd be down on the floor in a nap because I wasn't sleeping much in my shaky cabin in the sky.

Once I got home, once I was up those stairs and into my room, I stayed. I kept a chair against the door because the lock was flimsy as the rest of the place, one of those types that could be pushed, and who would hear me?

I counted the days he'd be driving here after he figured out I wasn't around San Francisco. He'd have to borrow a car because he never had one of his own. One, two, one to stopover and then another, and then he was driving into the city with a big grin. He'd stop for a hamburger, and he'd tease the waitress and ask if she'd seen me. Like a scraggy bird, he'd say. Bony as hell with hair like a witch. She'd laugh, think him cute and wonder why he was looking for such an ugly girl. I imagined him striding just streets away from me in the night of cars rolling up and down the hill, a dark-edged giant standing before the bright windows of White Spot.

When we came west, we stopped in Denver with Sharon for a few weeks because Jack Kerouac spent time in the city. Richard was following him across the country, sidestepping into his footsteps. He was going to be a writer too, with his notebook and him writing down a sentence as we stood in a bar.

Sharon had been like me moving from house to house in Boston till she got longing for home and went back to Denver. She'll be a nurse when she's done studying. 'Serious women make me bored,' Richard said.

She couldn't handle him. 'I don't like the way he stares, like you just have to listen to him. He's a maniac.'

I thought at least I have someone who do you have?

Sharon said Richard was my twin, why I kept with him. But I don't have his eyes, so bright and violent I couldn't hold them for more than a moment. Mine were like Patty Hearst's after she got kidnapped. Even in the photo where she's holding a gun, her eyes are looking every which way.

I'd been gone from him two weeks. I was up in the cabin under the covers and my coat because the cold seeped through the wooden walls. So I was lying there, not sleeping but not awake either, when I heard a sound down below where there was nothing before. It was not walking exactly, not a grown man's deliberate footsteps. It kept going around the cabin, around and around, a scraping sound. I stayed still. I reasoned that Richard couldn't find me here. He wouldn't even know about here. And then the scraping dimmed and stopped, and there was only the rumble of Colfax like a distant ocean.

Next night it was the same and the next. I looked for footprints around the cabin but found none. The dirt looked scattered in places, so I wasn't dreaming the sounds. I had to know. I couldn't sleep if I didn't know. So I stayed up and kept my clothes on. When I heard the scraping I took my flashlight and a rotted plank I'd picked up in the yard. First I stood at the top of the stairs staring out, but I saw no one. I walked down and flashed my light around. The long trailer house was dark. Estelle had come back from her torch dancing to lie peacefully beside Henry. Then I saw a large brown dog that ran from my light past the trailer and into the street.

I felt unsettled by the dog so when Estelle beckoned as I came home from work holding my bag of food, I expected she'd say 'a man came for you and he's coming back'. I had never told them about Richard, never told them not to say about me. I started trembling as if I'd been dead and someone wired me alive for the first time since I'd been here.

She took my hand. Henry had gone into hospital again. It was his sitting all day, legs limp on the steel step of the chair, his back twisted, which made him liable to infections.

'Whenever he goes in I think he'll never come back.'

You'll be free I thought. She wasn't that old, maybe thirty something. She moved spry as Henry was prone, her rubber-doll face insistent. She said the men liked to touch her after she danced holding her torch and came down into the tables to serve. 'I'm not really dancing with fire.'

Estelle drew me into the trailer. 'You're happy up there?' she asked.

I nodded because I could see she was afraid she might lose me too.

'I told Henry, she'll just take to living there, her very own house with no neighbors to bother her.'

'Yes indeed. And it's taken to me.' I said nothing about the dog or the little noises in the room or the fear that the cabin would collapse with me mixed up in the pieces.

She sat opposite me, her eyes fixing me like her husband that first day, his hollowed-out face waiting for me to say yes. She talked about when Henry ran the hardware. My little cabin was all that remained of the business. 'Sometimes they come back, the customers,' she said.

I felt scared because I had thought no one knew about this barren place. I said if someone comes looking for me, a man with black hair and blue eyes, he might come.

She said, 'We don't want trouble.'

'But if he should come asking, you just say no. Please.'

'You got man trouble?'

Why did I say? Because saying always meant that he would find me.

'I got lucky with Henry. Such a steady man.'

That night I heard the dog again, running, then pawing the ground. When I came out at the top of the stairs, he stood staring at me for a moment then ran away. Maybe he had lived here once and was remembering the food he was given, the kind hands on his back when he whimpered, just a puppy and cute. All that was long ago and now he was a skinny brown dog, a plain dog who ran before he could be shooed away.

Sometimes I imagined he would stay and be my friend and look after me. I thought of him while I cooked oatmeal in the old ladies home, stirring the grey sludge and dishing it out while they sat around the table, those who could. One of them said to me, 'You're skinny. Skinny as anything.'

I had counted the days and now weeks before he'd be in Denver walking up and down Colfax, looking in MacDonald's and White Spot, asking in the evenings over a jug of margaritas in the Satire whether they'd seen me. 'She might call herself something else just to try it out. She's so crazy that way. Seriously I'm worried about her because she's not right in her head. And who knows what she'll do.' Never would they think that this honest speaking guy with the firm handshake and the well favoured face. Never would they think he could hit like iron or dangle a woman over a cliff just for fun.

So I didn't take Colfax if I could help it. I walked around the back streets to reach the old age home. Sometimes I walked far from where I lived just to come back to it. Once a man called out to me from the balcony of an apartment building, 'You like weed? You wanna come up for a smoke?'

I looked behind myself as I walked, and if I had to go to Colfax I walked fast. There were men like Richard, bearded men with bright eyes and smiles which wrapped around me. I was always seeing him and not seeing him as if he was ordinary, the man all men looked like. When I finally returned to my cabin, I'd walk around the yard like that brown dog making sure.

I met Estelle coming out for her torch dance evening at the restaurant where she is meat and drink to men. I asked how Henry was. She shook her head. 'He's poorly. If he goes I don't know what I'll do. Can't stay here can I?'

'Don't give up,' I said. Not yet. Not till Richard gives up and leaves Denver if he's here, if he is.

That night me in my cabin and she in her long trailer house and the dog running below, we could be out on the plains, settler women waiting for our men. I still shivered up there even though it was warming to spring. I was like the old ladies in the home who claimed the cold permanent in their bones. As I lay under the covers and my jacket, I thought maybe I'd go where I'd never been. I'd drive up those mountains behind the city. But I knew I could not live alone and that someday I'd go back and he'd be there.

Next day I skipped work and stayed in bed till noon when the glowing sky had worked its way into my room. I set an egg out on the little two burner stove, let it boil till the edges of the yolk were green and I could cut it into slices. I would no longer hide. I'd sit at the counter of White Spot in full view of the big front window. Bulls eye he'd say throwing his darts.

Henry came back one day rolling past me with a hand raised. Estelle was like a young girl with him, clinging on to the arm of the wheelchair in her bitty little dress. I saw how he kept her, how she was like something he held on a string, a bright kite fluttering above him and he only had to jerk it for her to come dancing down to him. She with the insistent stare on her round rubbery face, his shadowed face with never a smile. Perhaps if you're in a wheelchair you don't, but the old ladies smiled all the time, the ones not sleeping.

I phoned Sharon to find out if Richard had turned up. It was only the third time, but she sighed when she said no. 'You sound like you want him to come after you.'

'Just, it's been a month.'

'Maybe he's found some other woman. Lucky you.'

Maybe. Maybe he wanted nothing to do with me. I was like Estelle before Henry came home. Cut loose.

I began to walk openly up Colfax, even stopping in bars where we had gone together. I can't hide forever, can I, and possibly, most likely, he's not around. But in a way I wanted to see a man with dark shorn hair turn around and smile at me. 'Got you,' he'd say.

I became the woman he told me I was. A man drinking from a pitcher of beer asked, 'You lost part of your head somewhere?' Because my eyes clouded when I looked up at the dark speckled ceiling of the bar. I climbed the hill of Colfax like I was walking into a picture, the mountains just cardboard, the store fronts flimsy as my cabin. All around me could collapse and fly away, and I would be left in wilderness.

Sometimes I thought how it might be if I killed myself. Could I be that brave? When I passed Henry, his corded arms turning and turning the wheels, I wondered if he thought about suicide.

34

'What you staring at?' he asked, 'Haven't you had your fill?'

I shook my head but he slapped the chair and rolled into the house, and I could hear Estelle call out to him, 'Honey?'

When they found Patty Hearst I thought, well nobody's come for me. I stopped into a phone booth and started to call Richard, got nearly to the end of the number before I hung up, scooped back my change.

That night the winds were strong around the cabin. I imagined the grasses on the plains stretching away from Denver, waving light feathery waves and my cabin rolling on the tide, the salty seaweed of the ocean pulling me back east and then letting me go.

I heard him again pawing around the yard. I was sure now he had lived here once and was coming back to the only home he knew. Then he barked. He'd never barked before. I thought Richard's come and the dog's warning me. The barking kept on. I was shivering under all my covers and clothes. He wouldn't stop, like he needed for me to come out. I put my jacket over my pyjamas, unlocked the door and stood up there at the top of the stairs.

The trailer house was lit up and I saw Henry in the yard. 'Scat,' he yelled at the dog. Maybe the dog didn't know what to make of a man in a wheelchair. He barked and barked. And then Estelle came out and clapped her hands at the dog. He bounded down the passage and was gone.

Henry saw me standing up there. 'You afraid of him?'

I said I'd seen him before.

'He won't be coming back,' he said, 'No way.'

KATHLEEN DONKIN

Open House

My father keeps a bear. This is not a thing that you tease or pet. I am in the habit of looking out of the window for it, left and right, before going outside. The bear follows my father around the back yard. In the evenings my father comes in for supper and then goes back out again and the two of them stand around out there, my father smoking and gazing at the sky and the trees, the bear nearby sniffing the air. The bear is big and solid as a baby elephant, the long fur on its back poked up like tines in damp weather.

We don't discuss the bear. There are a number of things concerning my family that we don't do, things I've never seen and that in fact don't happen: my father doesn't comb his hair in public, my mother doesn't eat cold cuts, my sister is never happy for long, we don't give parties, etcetera. The bear is not a subject. It doesn't even have a name.

I'm the oldest. My skirts and winter coats are handed down to my sister, Arles, who has her own ideas about what's attractive and disposes of them somehow.

'Plaid!' she says, like a curse word under her breath. Even so, I keep my things a long time, especially clothes. I keep them nice.

Arles stands in front of the mirror in the mornings, getting ready for school. She does her hair up and takes it down. Her appearance is crucial. 'I hate my feet,' she says. She is nervous, sometimes cruel, often inconsolable.

Arles and I are not alike. We're Day and Night mother says. We don't even remember the same things. Arles doesn't remember the Sunday drives in autumn, all of us together in the fat black French car. My mother sometimes drove. She knew how to shift the gears. She'd say, 'Let's see where we end up.' She liked to look at us in the back seat. I knelt to watch out the window. I remember how the upholstery smelled.

'You do not,' Arles says. Arles was only a baby. My mother used to go out a lot then, often by herself. Sometimes she drove all the way to the shore. My father never did groceries.

36

'Liar' my sister says. She refuses to believe anything I say.

My mother named my sister for a town in France where Vincent van Gogh once lived. My mother loves him; if Arles had been a boy she would have been called Vincent. I was named after my mother's mother's oldest friend, a woman who was in a wheelchair by the time I met her, at six. My name was meant to please my grandmother. It did not. It puzzled her. 'Marian is such a *brown* name,' was what she said.

My mother was a collector before she stopped going outside. Everything in this house, it seems, started out somewhere else in the world. Soapstone seals carved by Inuits, tapestries from Egypt and rugs from the Middle East – from provinces in countries that have since been subdivided and renamed. There are Chilean miniatures painted on wood and rare English coins set in brown velvet and a Chinese lamp with blue dragons. There are fishes with whiskers hand-painted on platters from Germany. When I was small, my mother would set some new thing on the heavy beam over the fireplace and say it had waited a long time and traveled a long way to live with us. My mother sees herself as a guardian of these things only; the Chinese lamp and the Greek pot and all the other things do not really belong to her. They'll stay with her she says, until she passes them on to me and Arles, when we're old enough to treasure and protect them as she does. She claims for herself only one or two careful reproductions of some sacred things – a grinning hump-backed man on a llama or a tortoise with an intricately carved shell. These are faithful to the originals, formal in their detail – gleefully alien, human artifacts. But for the originals my mother is only a caretaker and lover.

My mother's brother-in-law has just died. He lost his balance, my Aunt Kitty said, when she called from Charlottesville. His eyes opened wide and he clutched at the breakfast table in front of him like a boy on a roller coaster and then crashed out of his chair and died on the kitchen floor. My mother is preparing herself for going outside, for leaving the house, for 18 or 20 hours in the car, eating in fast food places, using public bathrooms and sleeping elsewhere. It has taken her mind off Uncle Wallace's death I think.

In a little while my mother and father will be on their way to Charlottesville and I will be in charge. Already though, I'm thinking of things, trying to anticipate the next three-and-a-half days. I've hardly thought about Aunt Kitty and Uncle Wallace except to try to imagine that degree of dizziness that would make a person fall out of a chair. He had no last words. He was Aunt Kitty's second husband and for that he seems less related to us. He taught math at a college. Aunt Kitty's house is small and plain and smells as good as new gloves. My aunt does not collect things. Her living room is very neat. There are several shades of beige and a painting over the sofa that seems religious but may not be. There is no clutter except for a few extra pillows she has embroidered with owls and squirrels. She once mentioned that her curtains are fireproof. My aunt is practical and kind and I'm ashamed that I haven't given her loss more thought. I will. There are other things at the moment, more pressing.

Arles walks into the kitchen. She looks at my mother and me and makes toast.

'When are you going?' she says. That's all she wants to know.

'Daddy and I are leaving in a few minutes. We'll be back on Monday.' My mother is exhausted with dread. She says nothing about Arles's outfit for school. Arles has rolled up the waistband of her skirt to make her legs look longer. 'Marian's in charge' my mother says for about the tenth time. Arles bends down to inspect herself in the side of the toaster.

Arles is planning a party. She's calling it an 'open house' and pretends not to see how ridiculous that is, and how dangerous. She is desperate to give a party. As soon as she heard about the funeral she started making plans. Nearly everyone at school knows about the party and feels invited. They're looking forward to it. There is renewed interest in the bear. My sister has drawn up a map of directions to our house. 'Up the hill' it says. 'Just keep going!' It's an adventure they'd pay for if they had to. They want to see the third floor of our house and the barn and my mother's collection of records. The bear I suppose they expect to be toothless and bald in patches, safely behind bars. They've lost the terror they had as kids when they'd be driven to our house to play and driven away again, never to return. I'm certain they're looking forward to walking up to the bars of the cage they've imagined, and giving it a good poke, seeing what it will do.

My mother kisses us goodbye. My father puts on his sunglasses and pats his breast pocket to check for cigarettes. My mother will not drive or even look at a road map. She can't help, he's got all the driving and directions to do. Even the radio will probably be hard for her although she won't complain. Turning off the radio will be one more thing my father will have to figure out. 'Goodbye girls,' he says, and pats his pocket again. Secretly he enjoys the challenge. I know this because he does more than he has to, he'll compute the mileage and have the air in the tires checked several times. He doesn't mind funerals but he wouldn't go unless he had to, unless he could do all the driving and figuring. Neither of them would be doing this without the other.

Arles is especially affectionate to them. She walks them out to the car and closes the door for my mother. I see her point through the window glass to the door lock. My mother locks her door. Arles walks along beside the car as my father backs it up. She's holding onto the door handle. When they start to pull away she kisses her fingers and touches the window. Twice, one for each. I feel like a traitor, knowing about the party and not saying anything. I wave from the terrace. I wish with all my heart that Arles would call it off.

Not a chance. After school Arles comes straight home. She removes a package of balloons from under the dishtowels and blows them up, one at a time. She ties a string on each balloon and goes outside, disappearing down the driveway without a word, completely absurd with a handful of balloons. The balloons, then, are not for the house, they're for the old mailbox post at the bottom of the hill. This is so nobody misses the turn-off.

There's nothing but mud and not a leaf on a tree. The woods around the house are spiky and colorless and this is neither the time nor the place for a party. The bear is nowhere in sight for the moment. Not that she cares. I mean, of course she cares, I was the one who coached her in walking right past it when going outside was unavoidable. I know she cares. I told her that bears can smell fear, the way cows can smell the current in electric fences. I drilled it into her about looking out the window both ways before going outside. Today though, the bear is nothing and she wants me to see that. She's determined. She goes right outside.

I have not always been afraid of the bear. I used to run outside, not stopping to look, when I saw my father coming up the drive. He'd shut off the car and get out slowly. He's not a hugger or a talker. 'Well,' he'd say, 'holding down the fort, Marian?' I'd always say 'yes,' pressing my finger into the mud-caked wheel well of the sedan and he'd say, 'Oh?' like another question, keeping his eyebrows up and looking around for the bear. 'That's right,' he'd say, extending the tips of his fingers to the top of my head and twisting around to see behind himself. He wouldn't mention the bear at all, even back then, even jokingly. He'd look all around, roll up the car window slowly and say, 'That's fine.'

I have tried to love the bear. I haven't gotten angry at it for crushing the daffodils or terrifying me. The worst I do is ignore it, try to hurt its feelings, try to impress on it the connection between what it does and how I treat it. I'm not sure it has feelings. You can't train a bear. They're stupid and impossible to punish and besides, this bear was full grown before anybody thought to say 'no' to it. It had three-inch claws and pointed teeth and weighed more than all of us together before we even thought of it as a bear at all, never mind laid down the law.

We've adjusted. We're careful not to make noise when it's napping. We fill in the holes it digs in the yard and apologize if it lowers its head and wags it at someone, growling. The mailman refused to deliver to our house years ago, and my father got a box at the Post Office. The garbage collector stopped coming too, of course, and my father bought a pickup and hauls the trash to the town incinerator himself.

It's reasonable to wonder why my father has not gotten rid of the bear. It's true we've had to go out of our way for it. We each do our part but nobody does as much as my father. How can we complain if he doesn't? I see how hard he works and how deeply resistant my father is to drastic solutions. My father has tried different approaches to the problem of the bear. For example, he tries to teach it what not to do, like bite the car tires, or break into the barn. My father keeps a stick with him at all times. He uses the stick to tap the bear on the nose, the absolute only place a bear is likely to experience pain.

'Bad!' he says. He uses a long branch for this job. Tap tap. 'Bad!' The bear lowers its head and looks ashamed. My father is pleased. I can tell by the look on his face that he's glad and relieved and hopeful and plans to teach the bear a second thing. We don't discuss it. We need some results first. We need to get a little momentum going. Our adjustments are ordinary routine now, unnoticeable, and it's like the bear has always been with our family.

I stand in the living room for a while, just looking at everything, like this is my last day on earth. Or I'm a tourist. Already I feel sorry. The party is a few hours away still, to allow for sunset and the unlikely possibility that my father and mother decide to turn around. If we knew they were coming back early, Arles or I would have to sit at the bottom of the hill somehow and turn people away.

My mother's things are everywhere. I press very gently on the lowest limb of the bonsai cedar. Who knows how old the tree is. It was a present to my mother more than fifteen years ago from a woman she used to know. The tree in the shallow dish is its own world, one of a thousand small, fixed planets in our house. My mother's friend held the tree low for me and invited me to feel the dampness of the earthenware dish. We have not seen her since. Without the bonsai, what do we have of my mother's friend? Of myself testing the damp? Of a single late afternoon when a visitor in a sky-blue wool suit arrived unexpected with a gift?

I touch the cheek of the small ivory mask and set the pair of tiny brass ducklings see-sawing on the cobra's nose. I close and open the hinged wooden triptych that depicts the festival of a holy day somewhere in Peru. The women wear derbies. The scowling baby in the foreground and the white dog trotting past exist nowhere else in the world and without my mother might have been lost or ruined. The heavy glass paperweights with the gardenias and butterflies worried me when I was little. Arles still hates them. The butterflies are preserved in the act of almost flying away. The gardenia petals have flecks of pollen. All real, my mother likes to say. In the corner of the room is a small etching of birds next to a framed photograph of my mother and me when I was three or four, sitting in a wheelbarrow. It's astonishing, suddenly, my mother in a wheelbarrow of all things and laughing, her cheek pressed to mine. There's a picture of my sister and me in matching pom-pom hats sucking icicles. Arles was always tall, and sometimes people mistook us for twins. I'm innocent. Whatever happens, I had nothing to do with this party.

It's dark. There is no sound. I'm in my room upstairs and my sister is in another part of the house, probably putting out potato chips and ashtrays or whatnot. Neither of us has any experience with these things. We're not speaking. We're waiting for whatever happens next.

They seem to arrive all at once. The house is pierced with voices from everywhere. Footsteps pound on the hardwood floors and up and down the stairs. Doors slam inside and out. I go to the window and look down. Headlights illuminate the front door and the lawn; silhouettes cut back and forth, breaking the beams. There's constant laughing suddenly, the girls are like those dolls with a pull cord in the back, making the same sound over and over. It must be what people do at parties. Car engines idle with a kikikiki sound, sending a gritty exhaust into the glare of the lights. Maybe they're about to leave. Maybe they've just stopped by and can see that the party is a bore and won't stay. Music blares out from the wing of the house most brightly lit. I know for a fact that my sister has never worked the stereo in the living room before. I can see from the upstairs window that there's hardly enough room for all the people that have come.

I stay in my room, door bolted. Every few minutes I pray for the party to stop, for everyone to lose interest. I try to read, but it's no good. Even

41

after a couple of hours, people are still arriving. There are horns and car doors slamming constantly and a steady stream of headlights wobbling up the rutted driveway in the dark. We have no neighbors or this would've been reported hours ago. How long do parties last? How are they ended?

I imagine that if I open my door the crowd smoking and shrieking outside on the landing will come flooding into my room like a dam burst. I try to imagine them standing in my room, seeing my things. Everything in my room is questionable suddenly since I don't know what other girls' rooms look like. I don't know if they have any of their old toys, what books they read, what they talk about. I have no friends in all the people that have come. This is not a terrible thought. Arles is here, somewhere, even if she is faking everything.

'Marian's in charge.' The thought of my mother's sad, quiet voice, her faith in me, her tender, painstaking love of beautiful things seizes me with fear. If a thought can stop my heart, this thought can. I run to look in the mirror and then open my door.

Two boys are peeing in the blue bathroom across the hall, door open. A group of older girls is on the staircase outside my bedroom. They're famous for cutting classes, for leaving school, for getting black eyes, for shrieking, even at teachers. I've seen them only from a distance, in the high school parking lot, sitting on cars. Close up, amazingly, it seems they've sat on the upstairs landing for years, smoking and surveying the crowd.

Downstairs is packed, wall to wall. I push my way through. I must be completely invisible. No one sees me, no one sees how wildly wrong this is, how terrible it is some 12th grader is in my mother's bedroom, sitting backwards on her chair at her dressing table, his beer bottle sweating on the glass top of the vanity among her atomizers. He's having a conversation with another boy, who is stretched out on her bed, his sneakers on the silk throw.

I will report this. I will tell what I saw, accept punishment for my part, for not speaking up sooner.

There are people in every room. In my father's dressing room is a boy with a chain across one shoulder sharing a small pipe with a girl who dropped out of Choir last year. He's got a motorcycle and a police record, that I know. The closet door is ajar and one of my father's shoes is visible.

The noise is tremendous the closer I get to the living room. There isn't room for another human being. The sofa is buried. One of the boys on the back of it leans against the wall, his stringy hair tilted into the still life of chrysanthemums. They've made a fire in the fireplace with damp logs that smoke badly. It's hard to breathe. In the kitchen two girls are crying and giggling and sharing one of the Wedgwood teacups for an ashtray. Nobody pays attention to them or to a curly-haired boy who sits at the table staring, not moving at all. Somebody has thrown up in the wastebasket in my father's study.

I can't stop moving. I go around and around, up and downstairs. There's nowhere to stop. It's exhausting but it seems essential to keep moving, watching everything, even if I can't do anything about it. I'm waiting for massive flames or some authority to show up and stop everything.

'Hey,' somebody says to me on the stairs to the third floor. It's a boy with brown hair and a beard, somebody who graduated already. He's got his arm around a girl whose nickname is Boo. The boy looks at me. 'Hey,' he says again. 'You're Arles's sister, aren't you?'

None of the rooms on the third floor is used anymore. It's where the old porch is, with its huge screened windows looking out over the woods. The play porch was for rainy days. The third floor is also where the housekeeper's room is. I still think of it as Looly's room, the one who lasted the longest. I open the door to Looly's room very slowly, no noise, the way I did when I was little and hoped to catch her praying. The room seems empty at first. The oak leaves and acorns carved into the headboard of the bed gleam in the moonlight, like the shiny eyes of trapped nocturnal animals. There is a sound from the bed. A bare rear end rises from the mattress behind the footboard and then disappears. A girl makes a noise, a grunt like someone agreeing. I step back into the hall, pulling the door closed. I want to run to the old porch that's freezing this time of the year and lock myself in. There's an old fur coat hanging there I could keep warm in. I want to fall asleep and wake up when everyone is gone.

Suddenly screaming starts outside, screaming and voices shouting. From the old sewing room window I can see out onto the driveway and back yard. I open the window and stick my head out. Kids are pouring out of the house and rushing across the terrace onto the driveway. A crowd gathers noisily inside the terrace lights, with others climbing onto the car hoods and straining to see around each other. Some of the cars are turned in a half-circle around the driveway.

In the center of the headlights is the bear. Its head is lowered and wags slowly from side to side, blinking in the glare of the headlights. It shakes its head calmly and sniffs the air. A beer bottle hits it, and falls to the ground unbroken, spilling. The bear sniffs and then licks it tentatively. Fresh screaming is mixed with laughter then and more things start flying through the air, pizza crusts, cigarette butts flicked and arcing like lightning bugs, stones, sticks from the top of the woodpile, and then girls' shoes. The girls are howling for their shoes and trying to keep from sliding off the cars, the boys yanking their legs and feet. Shoes are hitting the bear on all sides, hard. The boys are throwing them like fastballs, aiming for the face. The bear turns and turns each time a shoe hits it. It ducks its head and shakes it again and again, as if a cloud of biting flies were attacking. The boys are less afraid now. In the dark the kids are unrecognizable, squatting and hollering on the car hoods and roofs in groups or leaning out of the car windows.

A rock pulled out of the stone wall hits the bear on the side of its head. The bear staggers sideways and wags its head again, then rears up on its hind legs. Screaming, the kids leap from the cars and rush from the dark towards the lighted terrace and the house. The bear's front legs swipe the air, paws big as dessert plates, the long claws visible. Another rock catches it in the ear. The bear falls over softly and then rights itself again, the rock that hit it shattering one headlight of a car behind it. The bear lunges forward, and makes for a car, scrabbling to climb in the window, its claws raking the sides. It plunges one foreleg through the open window. Its rumbling breaths are audible, even from the upstairs window, the deep, angry bellows chuffing under the screech of its nails against the side of the car and all the shrieking.

Enormous bangs, like guns firing, rupture the night, as boys start hurling firecrackers from the terrace. The explosions rattle the windows. A firecracker explodes inside the ring of abandoned cars. Somebody screams that the bear is inside one of the cars and more firecrackers explode in a volley nearby. Someone else shouts that the bear is nearer, under the bushes around the terrace. Panicking again, a mass of kids plunges back through the door and into the house all at once. The bear is seen everywhere in the dark, behind the terrace wall, up in the beech tree, between cars. The bear has red eyes. The bear is two bears.

Some boys chance it, scrambling back into cars, closing the windows quickly and gunning the engines. They try to move the cars around to find the bear, to run it down. But they can't, the cars are packed in tight, every which-way. They give it up, tossing the firecrackers they have left towards the woods. There are bursts of pink light before the firecrackers run out. They blast the car horns for good measure. For a second it's quiet. Then somebody growls and laughs. There is more growling and laughing, kids making bear claws with their hands and chasing each other back outside, and across the terrace.

There's nothing left to eat or drink and people are leaving. Some girls are looking for their shoes in the driveway, holding onto each other, or onto their boyfriends, afraid of stepping on broken glass. They're trying to see where they're going, waving their cel phone lights over the ground. Just before morning, the last cars start up. There's yelling and doors slamming and they leave. One by one all the cars drive away.

I start turning the lights on in every room on each floor. I want to see everything. Water has been left running in one of the upstairs bathrooms and there is a sour smell. I crank open the window and let the air in, imagining it rushing into the house like a swollen stream, filling the rooms and eddying hard in the corners, gushing through the weave of the curtains and the soiled, sheet-covered mattress in Looly's room, churning under the ceilings where smoke has collected for hours and still stinks. No bodies, anywhere, though I'm prepared for it. The play porch is still undisturbed, the enormous windows facing serenely into the dark hills and lightening sky, an empty room, a room for make-believe. It occurs to me for the first time that I would be very happy to live forever in such a room, on a high floor, in a big city.

The morning light is still dim, but it's peaceful. I walk very slowly, looking all around, floor by floor, and taking shallow breaths. I keep my eyes open. Pillows are flat and glasses and plates of food and empty beer bottles are everywhere.

Arles is slumped in a kitchen chair, holding her head. More dirty glasses and oil-stained paper plates are all over the table. Ashtrays loaded with cigarette butts and wads of gray chewing gum and bits of bologna and crackers are stacked, one on the other. Somebody did this for Arles before taking off, piled things in one place. The silence is abrupt. It makes things seem worse than maybe they are.

Arles turns her head and moves her hand away from her mouth. She drank too much. 'Is it over?' she asks. Even with her hair coming down and pale looking, she's prettier than me.

'Yes.'

Arles turns her head and covers her face again. I make my way into the living room, the epicenter of the destruction. I have no expectations,

I just put one foot in front of the other, still alive, not grateful or heartbroken, like the tornado victims I've seen on tv, walking around in a daze. I pick the sofa pillows up off the floor and fit them back onto the sofa. I switch off the power to the stereo and sweep up an old 78 that got stepped on. Bing Crosby. I open the windows for more air. I try to reassure Arles. 'It's okay,' I call through the doorway. 'We can put everything back.'

I wonder what was stolen, how long it will be until the loss is discovered. 'Such and such is missing' my mother will say one day. She'll look and look. We all will. It's gone now, whatever it is.

LESLEY KRUEGER

Steroid Dreams

Phil heard the specialist say cancer. The words probably and cancer. She was temporizing, saying something like, It probably isn't cancer, but Phil knew they led you toward it gently, steering the discussion from maybe to probably to set your affairs in order. Not that it could be called a discussion with Phil pinned to the dental chair, Dr. Chin's latex-covered fingers pitty-patting over his bleeding gums. Mouth cancer. Which he'd had to mention himself.

'I understand your concern,' she'd said, 'but it probably isn't cancer.' Bowing out his lower lip with one latex finger: 'I'll be doing a biopsy, a little snip, but I think what we're going to find is a nice ripe case of lichen planus.'

Biopsy. There it was. Phil considered the operatic irony of the host of a national radio show being diagnosed with cancer of the mouth. Freud had died of it, father of the talking cure. Like Phil, Freud had been a smoker, which not only explained the cancer, but gave him an additional authority when pointing out that addictions like smoking were a substitute for masturbation. The line through Freud, talking, smoking, masturbation, and from there to allegations from Phil's few, embittered and demonstrably sociopathic critics that he tended to wank on during his opening monologues – Phil had to admit it wasn't a clear line, not precisely diagnostic, but the word cloud undoubtedly had cancer at its core, and contained an element of divine justice. He probably had cancer and he probably deserved it.

On the other hand, he'd never heard of lichen planus. And surely nothing could be more absurd, more undignified, than growing a crop of lichen in your mouth.

He was rehearsing for his friends, of course. Years of interviewing politicians had sharpened Phil's ear for the lie. Dr. Chin didn't think he had cancer. If she'd shown even the faintest hint of worry, he would have been terrified, been gibbering. One time his GP had prodded his prostate and looked grim.

Of course I look grim, he'd said. I've got my finger up your arse.

* * *

'Oral lichen planus is a chronic inflammation of the tissue on the inside of the cheeks, gums and/or tongue that is thought to be auto-immune in nature.'

Phil left the periodontal office with his lower lip pouting like a model's. In his hand was an info sheet handed him by the hygienist, an inexplicably pink piece of paper topped by a smiling cartoon tooth.

'For reasons we don't know, our immune systems sometimes attack our own bodies. In this case, the attack can cause lacy, white raised tissue and/or red patches in your mouth. Its resemblance to lichen is why we call it lichen planus. The condition is most common in middle-aged people, and associated with stress. It can be successfully controlled by the use of topical corticosteroid ointments and/or mouthwashes.'

The former copy editor in Phil wanted less and/or. He wanted a definition of controlled and successful. These were important words. His professional success was tied up in his ability to control himself on air, letting out calibrated puffs of empathy, irony, curiosity or anger as demanded by his million-plus listeners, whose needs he intuited minutely; his audience an itch he was bound to scratch.

On the other hand, his marriage to Mei Li felt increasingly out of control as she demanded more empathy and curiosity than Phil could muster after seven years and the birth of twins. Graham and Corbett had emerged in a heroic labour four years ago looking like wrinkled Chinese versions of Phil. Since then, he'd parented his boys with an abject and uncomprehending pride that Mei Li was prone to call inept. Lack of control, lack of success: home had become the opposite of work. At least if you left aside Phil's growing urge to scratch a familiar itch.

'Lichen planus can be successfully controlled with corticosteroids.' The quote burred in his head as he pulled into traffic. In dictionary terms, successfully implied a lesser victory than conquered; controlled a lesser success than eradicated. Both were second best, Phil thought, wondering whether he had a second marriage or a second-best one.

He pictured his two children with Lorraine. Counting on his mental fingers, he made Nora twenty-two and just about to graduate from art school. Bobby was eighteen and a male version of Lorraine, who was as beautiful as ever. He had once thought Mei Li beautiful. She still was.

* * *

'My God, that's awful. Chronic? What's it going to do to your teeth?'

He wouldn't mention his cancer fears to Mei Li. She looked him over with big darting eyes, her pony-tail swinging. Mei Li was seventeen years younger than he was. A third-generation Canadian, although she and her brothers were given Chinese names after their father, a statistician, had gone from Wayne back to Bing Wen: what he called a regression toward the mean. Mei Li's brothers were now Gord and Duncan, but she'd kept the name her father had chosen. Her mother had been implacably Evelyn, at least until she'd died in a car crash when Mei Li was ten years old.

'The periodontist said I'll be fine. Back eating curries before Christmas.'

Mei Li sat down abruptly, as if things had got too much. The final nudge over the edge; the straw and camel's back. The twins were ominously quiet in their bedroom. Something was ready to give.

'It's actually quite funny,' Mei Li said, a smile fighting its way to the surface. 'The radio host with hoof and mouth disease.'

'I think the word you're looking for is ironic,' Phil said, sitting down beside her.

'I need to go back to work.'

'You're bored?'

'No, but I'm getting boring. I was sure it was cancer. I *never* catastrophize.'

'I've never been able to pronounce that.'

Mei Li was a physiotherapist. Phil had put out his back at a low point in his first marriage.

'My salary would barely cover the cost of day care,' she said.

'Why your salary? They're my sons, too.'

Who were far too quiet.

'You'll have to stop breast-feeding,' he said, picking his way onto egg shells.

A quick swivel toward him, Mei Li's eyes hardening, then going soft. She kissed him and fixed his collar, which the dental torture had no doubt crimped. The freezing was wearing off and the snip in Phil's gums was throbbing like a lighthouse beacon. She must have seen the grey of his face behind his greying beard. Her sick old husband.

'You're right. You've probably been right for a while.'

Phil brightened. So there were advantages to illness.

'Of course, you're going to have to quit smoking.'

Mei Li really ought to go back to work. She *was* getting boring. For some reason, he'd assumed when they met that a physiotherapist would have a simple, open, physical personality. She would be a relief from the elusive and maddening Lorraine, whose artistic career had been taking off at the time, along with her ego. He had overlooked Mei Li's obsessive qualities and been flattered by her jealousy. Like her hair, she was often coiled.

'The boys are far too quiet,' he said.

'I murdered them.'

Phil's heart jumped. Curtains parted and he saw her as being capable of murder, a lurid vision that didn't quite dim when Mei Li laughed at her joke and leaned against him. Phil knew he was being absurd, but he couldn't relax until he heard the familiar sounds of brotherly love from the bedroom. A crash. A scream. 'Mommy! He bit me!'

'You rest,' she said, when Phil made to get up. It was true: she was exhausting. He loved his beautiful young wife. He was getting old.

* * *

In his dream, Phil was running. The world was hyper-real, the buildings on either side of the road solid and subtly coloured, pale poured concrete skins that ballooned toward him, rounded and swelling toward the sunken black ribbon of road. Then they breathed in, turning concave as their skins withdrew toward their elevator spines before swelling out again.

Buildings breathing on the edge of the road, and Phil knew they were not only buildings but dinosaurs with leathery pockmarked skin, beasts so huge he couldn't see their heads, only their enormous trunks half sunk into the earth. This was remarkably beautiful, the world burnished and alive.

But Phil was running away from something, and he had to run faster, forced along by the piston action of his mechanical knees. He had no idea where the knees had come from. Steel knees forcing him to run, panicking him as the buildings rumbled and started to rise, shaking free of the earth…

* * *

Phil jerked awake. Bolt upright in bed, heart pounding. He was having a heart attack. No, he'd had a nightmare. Heart attack. Nightmare. He took his pulse, finger on his neck, pound pound pound pound. Rapid heartbeat: tachycardia. In his job he picked up random words. Vocabulary. He picked up random facts, his knowledge broad but shallow. He was a shallow man whose heart wouldn't stop pound-pound-pounding.

A shroud of pressure tightened across his shoulders. He *was* having a heart attack. Certainly not panic. He hadn't had a panic attack in years. He checked his heart rate on his phone, one hundred twenty beats per minute. Mei Li slept deeply beside him. Both his wives were deep sleepers, Lorraine at peace with herself, Mei Li exhausted by the twins. He didn't want to disturb her. Felt too foolish to disturb her: a panicky old git with 4 a.m. fears. Instead he padded to the bathroom, slumping down on the toilet, a smooth porcelain chill through his Y-fronts.

It would be an indignity to be found dead on the toilet, but men were, at least in Philip Roth novels. Was it Roth? Phil felt a Pavlovian reaction: toilet, sitting, drop your drawers. He didn't strain but there was a howl of agony from his haemorrhoid, Hubert. It hurt far more than the pressure across his shoulders, when surely a heart attack would be excruciating. His heart rate was down to ninety beats per minute, although his knees were shaking uncontrollably. That and his bowels: it was a panic attack. Phil breathed in and out like the buildings in his nightmare. Wiped blood.

In his study, he typed *steroids nightmare panic attack* into his laptop and pulled more than a million hits. Reading through the misspelled howls of agony, Phil got on top of himself, his knees going still, the tightness across his shoulders receding as his muscles relaxed. He'd started the steroid cream ten days ago and had been elated not only by the effect on his crop of lichen but by a hit of energy so pristine it had to be chemical. Now the steroids had thrown him into overdrive. 'Lichen planus can be successfully controlled by...' He still wanted a definition of success. A cigarette. One day he'd quit.

Heart rate: seventy-two. The worst was over. It was 4:19 in the morning and he'd had a panic attack, his first since the year of the divorce. It was probably caused by the medication, confirming his status as a soulless bag of chemicals. Sitting at his desk in the penumbral gloom, Phil took a long fall into the emptiness of life. A breeze blew through his ribs, the knowledge of mortality, of Death in his skinny black suit leaning against the tree outside, or maybe waiting in the long-closed video store down the block, screening old Quentin Tarantino movies.

Phil was a household name, beloved across the country (especially in the small-town demographic), sitting atop a skyscraper like the huggy cousin of King Kong. He had a beautiful wife, a beautiful ex, four children so handsome his genes would be replicated unto future generations, rendering him immortal. His children's beauty came from his wives, but at least he got to pass on his Y chromosome, and to his

51

daughter Nora's kids, if he'd got the genetics right, his lack of male pattern baldness.

And that was it. Phil was fifty-one years old and that was it. He couldn't afford any more offspring and wouldn't rise any higher in his profession. He'd seen what happened to friends who'd tried their luck in the U.S. and couldn't fool himself into believing he would do any better. He was a national icon in a small, unimportant nation. A radio host, for God's sake. All he could look forward to was trying to hold onto what he had, and ultimately failing, and that was the definition of life.

* * *

The actress clicked quickly out of the studio on her red-soled high heels. She had rather sweetly crossed her legs so he would see her expensive soles, but he'd been not-nice to her, asking left-field questions of someone contractually bound to promote a film she might well hate. Judging by the trailer, she should.

'When you say you hope you're successful in conveying your character's horror,' he'd asked, and she'd nodded vigorously, 'how do you define success?'

Now the new chase producer slipped in to discuss his next guest, on after the pre-recorded segment now playing. The producer was twenty-three. They all looked twenty-three, even the ones who were thirty. This one might even have been twenty-two, and she was pretty in a sturdy blond Dutch kind of way. Not that Phil ever pissed in the well where he got his drinking water. Or to put it in corporate-speak, was ever guilty of sexual harassment. He had his standards.

'It's interesting,' she said, 'the way your obsessions kinda skew the interviews. Success, I mean.' Phil was tactically open with his staff about his preoccupations, letting them see him as human, and therefore to be forgiven. 'It makes me wonder the extent to which journalists' personal lives more or less impinge on the national agenda.'

Oh, so she'd figured that out. Good doggie.

'What did you just call me?'

Phil took off his headphones and rubbed his eyes. 'I'm in the middle of another mid-life crisis,' he said. 'You're going to have to bear with me.'

Through the half-open door, he could see his next guest, her bristles of flagrantly dyed red hair. Cochineal, he thought. Made from dried Mexican insects. One of his guests had said the British Redcoats owed the colour of their uniforms to the importation of cochineal from Mexico in the late eighteenth century. However deep his angst, Phil loved the pinball nature of life, this leading to an unpredictable that.

'I asked her your question,' the producer said. He must be staring at the upcoming guest. 'Whether she prefers to be called an author or a writer. She said author.'

She'd failed, then. Pretentious. He wasn't going to be any easier on the author than the actress. It was one of those days.

* * *

His nightmare had come from the divorce. He and Mei Li had been leaving her apartment, although officially he'd been on a corporate retreat. Entwined with Mei Li, laughing, gelid with sex, lots of it, he'd done a double-take when seeing Lorraine across the street. She was just standing there, confirming her guess, letting him see her, then turning and walking away.

Phil tried to follow, but Mei Li clung to his arm. A tug of war, Phil pulling one way, Mei Li refusing to let go. 'Shit!' he cried, but when he saw her flat-out terror that he'd leave her, Phil gave in, feeling flattered, tender, and trapped.

At home, Lorraine looked like a dogwalker bagging a turd. Her new role as an edgy feminist artist involved half-shaved hair, tight jeans and kick-ass boots. She was as sexy as hell and he couldn't remember why he'd been unfaithful, aside from the fact they'd been together for almost twenty years, and that he suspected he bored her.

'How many is this, Phil?' she asked, in her breathy voice. 'I've lost track, if I ever knew. It's tedious, it really is, and the children are old enough they're going to start noticing. Why you don't always make the school concerts. It's not good for them to know you're a liar.'

He had no answer, and only asked for one final, normal outing with the kids before the talk. He'd promised Bobby a guitar, and took both kids to Long & McQuade, which since Phil's youth had been filled with intense crumpled youths longing for fame.

One look at Nora and the sales clerks raced over, testosterone jostling, the last man standing being a tall drink of water who'd won by going to Nora's high school, a black kid shy as a vole.

'A Gibson, sir,' the kid repeated.

'I'm cheap,' Phil told him, making Nora blush furiously.

'A Korean Gibson.' The kid was unperturbed and brought a guitar from a nearby rack. He handed it to Phil, an unspoken comment and a correct one. Bobby had no interest in playing guitar and was already sidling over to the drums.

Phil hadn't played in years, and found he could barely manage a chord. His wedding ring kept tripping him up, and he tugged it off impatiently, putting it on the amp.

'That should help,' he said.

Nora ignored him and the sales vole was busy worshipping her. Behind them, Bobby sat down behind a drum kit. With Phil hacking out a half-remembered melody, all of them were distracted, and the street kid must have seen this. There was a streak. A boy racing by, grabbing Phil's ring and pounding out of the store.

'Hey!' the sales kid cried. With a glance at Nora, he sprinted after the thief. And here's where the nightmare started: Phil sprinting after them. Not just standing there as stupidly as he'd done in life, but running and running, feeling increasingly panicked. Phil was himself but also the black kid dodging along a crowded street, and how would that be seen by the wrong cop? Phil had always hated himself for exposing the kid. For that and everything else.

'Did that guy just take your ring?' Nora asked.

Shrugging even more stupidly. 'It's only a ring.'

Bobby wasn't paying attention, having found a drumstick. But Nora stared at Phil, putting it together, and he felt his mouth crank into an awful shape.

He simpered, and his adored daughter gave him a look of disgust, walking over to her brother, shielding him; and it was among the chief tragedies of Phil's life that she'd had no use for him since.

* * *

Playing Lego on the floor with the twins. They weren't identical but they looked alike, Graham the leaner and more straight-ahead kid, more like Bobby, while Corbett was dreamy and sulky, improbably like Lorraine. They were building a city, Phil putting a palm tree on the roof of a skyscraper under Corbett's giggly direction. When Mei Li came in, Phil wondered what he was doing wrong, but she only handed him a scotch and clinked glasses.

'Your mother's a lush,' she told the boys, and Phil could see Graham storing that up. Mei Li ought to be careful, and she seldom was.

'That interview with the writer this morning,' she said.

'Author.'

'What a pill. What does she look like?'

Phil pictured the cochineal hair. 'Belligerently homely,' he said. 'One of those people who flaunt their lack of looks.' Sexual, he didn't say. Angry. Transparent. She'd reminded Phil of himself.

Lucy Verrall was the latest literary succubus of Virginia Woolf. In her award-winning novel, she riffed on her ancestral connection to Jacob Verrall, who had owned Virginia's country house before Virginia and her husband Leonard had bought it. Jacob Verrall had been an eccentric, tying a string from his foot to a bell in the orchard, letting him lie in bed and wiggle his toes to frighten the birds from his cherry tree. Lucy's novel went back and forth between the Verralls and the Woolves, bringing in a Hannah Verrall who had come to Canada in 1841, although Phil had lost interest by then and had no idea how she tied it all up.

'To start off,' the author said, muscling in as he finished his introduction, 'you haven't read the book, have you?'

'Yes, I have,' Phil answered blandly. 'And frankly what interested me most, although you give him short shrift in your novel, is Leonard rather than Virginia Woolf.'

Seeing she was about to interrupt, he went on, 'Reading your book sent me to Leonard Woolf's autobiography, which I imagine is what an author like yourself hopes for, an author authoring a book about writers' – she was glaring at him – 'to send your readers back to the works of the writers in question.'

'Now just a minute,' he said crankily, when she tried to interrupt again. 'If you're going to ask me a question, I'm going to answer it. And what impressed me most about Leonard Woolf was something he wrote when he was eighty-eight years old...'

'Five volumes of autobiography. That should tell you something about his hubris.'

'Adding up his contributions to founding the League of Nations and the British Labour Party, he estimated that during his very long life, he had put in between 150,000 and 200,000 hours on committee meetings and the associated writing. Yet he said that the world in 1969 would have been exactly the same if he'd spent his life playing ping-pong. He could see very clearly that he had achieved practically nothing.'

Holding her eye, Phil asked, 'How on earth can you justify writing another book about Virginia Woolf in the face of such humility?'

'Because I hate ping-pong,' Lucy Verrall replied.

55

'I thought hipsters liked it again.'

'Is it your job to tell an author what to write?'

'Well sometimes I can't help wondering,' Phil answered amiably.

* * *

That night, birds exploded from the swamp, the beat of their wings sounding like struck paper. A glossy purple bird. A tiny vermilion bird like a flung bindi. Black bird with white beak. Green bird, blue bird. A kaleidoscope of birds under the richest of skies.

Phil knew he was dreaming and knew this was Mexico. They'd gone there for a week's vacation with his friend Bob Trevor and Bob's second wife, Lucía. Phil had recently moved in with Mei Li, and it had been a relief to travel with another second coupling after the censure they'd faced. Not that Phil should have been travelling with Bob, who was a politician and a source, although Bob had lost his Parliamentary seat in the last election and Phil thought he could roughly justify the trip. He also didn't give a rat's about corporate rules on conflict of interest, not when Bob looked like day-old bread.

They had left their resort to rattle through the nearby town in a shit-box rental. Lucía was driving, the political wife who waded into crowds, managed residences, looked adoringly at her husband and threw herself into silences like a thumb in a dike. There had been more than a few silences on the trip, Mei Li having gone stone quiet, abashed in the company of people so much older than her, Bob not having married youth, but warm Mexican comfort.

'*Tope*,' Lucía cried, as the car reared up and dropped down abruptly.

'Speed bump,' Bob translated. 'It blew out the speedometer.'

'Now you can't see how fast I'm going.'

'Meaning the odometer isn't working, either.' Bob had become an avid birder, and they were heading toward a little-known nature preserve. The directions from the local branch of Lucía's family involved going to the village where her cousin Lupe used to live – not the last village, but the one before that – and turning left for eighteen clicks.

'It's okay. I can find it,' Lucía said, and soon they were driving past ranches, purple mountains to their left. They passed one small adobe town. Another. Roosters crowed and children ran in circles. Mei Li turning to stare at them. Wistfully, Phil noted, not without alarm. At the fourth village, Lucía slowed down.

'This can't be where Lupe lived,' Bob said. 'There isn't any left turn.'

'They meant where her old boyfriend came from,' Lucía said, and turned right.

About fifteen minutes after the turn-off, they reached an oblong of emerald green the size of a football field, a swamp in the middle of dried-up farmland. There must have been a spring feeding it.

'Stop!' Bob cried.

Lucía threw on the brakes.

'That might be a purple gallinule,' Bob said.

The swamp was painted with lily pads. Bob identified the elusive gallinule, a brilliant purple wader with long yellow legs. Getting slowly out of the car, they kept their binoculars trained. The bird was hunting in the reeds, probably for frogs, lifting one long leg delicately to reveal a yellow foot the size of a cupped hand. Bob pointed out a white-faced ibis nearby, and two green herons. On the top of a reed, a vermilion flycatcher.

A boy bicycled up, a slingshot on his shoulder, and dismounted to watch the crazy *gringos*. Before long, he said something in Spanish that made Bob brighten.

'He asked if we want to know the names of the birds,' Lucía said. 'This could be very privileged information, you see. He might tell us indigenous names.'

The boy nodded at some birds in the swamp that Bob had called black coots.

'*Pichichi*,' he told them.

'*Pi-chi-chi*,' Bob echoed, writing it down.

Nodding solemnly, the boy pointed to a common gallinule.

'*Se llama pato*.'

'It's called duck,' Lucía translated.

A barely perceptible pause, and Bob courteously wrote down '*pato*.'

It turned out the other birds were called duck, as well. The heron duck. The ibis duck. The purple gallinule duck. They all tasted like chicken.

Mei Li had remained quiet throughout. Now she approached the boy and managed with gestures and a few *pesos* to borrow his bike, slinging into the saddle and wobbling down the rutted dirt road.

'Her beautiful knees,' Lucía said, mourning the inevitable fall.

But Mei Li soon got the hang of it and began pedalling faster, circling, taking a run at a mammoth pothole like a pro rider, digging down at the start and flying out the far end, shouting with laughter, sending the birds flapping into the reeds.

'I'm bored out of my fucking mind!' she yelled.

'*La China loca!*'

'The crazy Chinese girl,' Lucía translated. 'You have a firecracker, Phil. What's the matter with her, underneath?' When Phil paused, Lucía said comfortably, 'That's all right. I'll get it out of her. It's probably the mother.'

Mexicans had called Mei Li the Chinese girl often enough that Phil already knew what it meant. Now he began to see her as china, delicate and perishable, white porcelain shards exploding from the bike and flying into his dream of birds, his kaleidoscope of colour, purple and vermilion blood spilling, slivers flying toward his open eyes...

* * *

Phil jerked up in bed. Tachycardia. Heart – no, panic attack. Sitting on the john, his knees shaking uncontrollably. Online research had shown that lichen planus could turn into mouth cancer. Hubert bled.

* * *

'Your author made sure to get in where she was doing her readings,' Mei Li said. 'Coast to coast.'

'I felt like the community bulletin board.'

'I kept picturing her as a wolverine. Vicious creature.'

'I wouldn't give her that much credit. She's more like a rotten tooth you can't stop prodding with your tongue.'

'Gross!' Graham shrieked happily.

'Daddy's tongue,' Corbett cried, and Mei Li gave Phil such a raw look he picked Graham up by the arms and swung him around the room, faster and faster.

'Not before bed!' Mei Li cried. 'My God, Phil. Four children. Haven't you ever learned *anything*?'

* * *

The second dream tonight. An enormous airplane turned belly up in a scrub ravine below the hotel, its wings held out like silver arms. He was there with his dead father, and they looked down at an open bay in the belly of the plane that was ready to receive...

* * *

Phil must have cried out.

'My God, what's the matter?'

Mei Li was instantly awake. Phil's heart was beating far too fast. He felt breathless, incapable, but knew he had to calm her.

'Nightmare. Been having them. Two. Tonight. Medication.' Phil broke down weeping. 'I have to take it. This could turn into cancer. But it gives me such godawful nightmares I'm scared of going to sleep. I don't know what to do.'

'You can't get cancer. You've got *children*.'

They clung to each other. This wasn't good for either of them. They weren't good for each other, presuming anybody was. But the definition of a successful life might be perseverance, and Phil didn't, he couldn't, let her go.

The Verrall book was on his bedside table. He'd resolved to read it so he wouldn't be a liar, at least retrospectively. The author had written a deeply affecting scene where Virginia and Leonard Woolf visited Freud, who was dying of cancer. Phil had checked this out, and it had happened. Freud gave Virginia a narcissus.

If Phil went to Lucy Verrall's reading, he would bring her a narcissus. But of course he wouldn't go.

KAREN ASHE

The Disappeared Girl

We were to call her Myrtle, she said, cos she didn't feel nothing like no Great Aunt. When supper was done, she lit the largest of the candles, then used that to light the others, poking at the curled-up wicks with the flame till the last of them was lit.

The dinner was lying heavy in my belly after seeing what Myrtle had done to the bird; one minute it was bok-bok-boking in the yard, next it was crisping in the smoking-hot skillet. Laurel's dead weight across my lap didn't help, but every time I tried to get out from under her she clung tighter, whining. Billy was playing *This Little Piggie*, with my feet, gripping my toes with his hot little hands.

To get into the rocker, Myrtle needed to hold on to her knees, for balance, or something, and she made a sound, somewhere between a sigh and a whistle, like when you blow through a blade of grass. The candles flickered some, stretching out their necks, then shrank to burn steady. An owl hooted, or it may have been the echo of the hoot we were hearing, we were so deep in the country. Billy stuck his thumb in his mouth. Myrtle snuck a peek at him as she tamped tobacco into her pipe. When she sucked on it her face fell in on itself.

Tell us a story. Billy's cheeks were pink from the sun, his eyes wandering the way they do when he's tired. *Mamma always tells us a bedtime story.* I was about to call liar, but Myrtle spoke first, smoke trailing every word.

A story, huh? Crickets cracked the silence. Seemed the darker it got, the hotter it grew. *Well, I don't know any fairy stories, for sure.* She polished her glasses on the hem of her skirt. *And you musta heard the one about the disappeared girl?*

Mamma and Our New Daddy roared off in a cloud of red dust, tyre-squeals standing in for a goodbye. We watched from the edge of the road until the Chevy was nothing but sunlight flashing on its fenders. Then the only thing between us and the blurry horizon was yellow grass and blue, blue sky. Great Aunt Myrtle shielded her eyes with her hand.

Was it a nice weddin?

60

It was like no lunch I ever had; brown soup that might've been mushroom, and not from a can, corn on the cob, hard-boiled eggs. The iced-tea was just tea. Ice never stood a chance.

I tried to Set a Good Example to Billy and Laurel. I cleared my plate, even though I had dust-grit in my back teeth. But they pushed their food around, sending me glares. As if it was my fault.

After a while Myrtle got up and opened the back door. She went outside, leaving us squinting at the sudden brightness. Billy looked at me and I knew he was about to start up. Then we heard a couple of rusty squeaks, and a sound like rain.

Myrtle was standing in the shade of an oak, a green, dirt-speckled hose in her hand. One end was attached to a rusty old tap, the other spurting silvery water into a tin bath.

Whoooheeee!!! Billy went hopping over the scorched grass, letting his t-shirt fly as he went. The tub wasn't even half full before he was hitching his leg over the side, naked behind white and jiggling.

I unhitched Laurel's legs from around my middle, prised her fingers from around her neck, but as soon as I put her down, she grabbed onto my ankles, howling, and once Laurel sets to howling there is no pacifying her. Her grip on my ankles was hot and sure. The water rattled into the tub. Grasshoppers shrieked.

That child sure is attached to you. It wouldn't kill you to take her awhile. I thought it, but didn't say it. *How old you now?* Standing side by side like that, our shadows on the grass reminded me of paper dolls we'd made at school, don't remember which one. Fold a piece of paper, over and over. Draw a person on it, cut round it. Then, unfold the paper, and there's a whole string of them, identical, all joined together at the elbow, or the foot, or head. You have to keep to the lines, one slip of the scissors and the whole thing will just fall to pieces.

Eleven and a half. Myrtle went inside, returning in an instant with a washed-out old slip in her hand. *Here. This oughta fit. It's old, but ain't nobody wore it but me.* You could tell it was white to start with, but now it was no-colour and had scuzzy marks on it where the iron must've stuck. Hand-me-downs. All the same. The water in the tub looked so cool, and I was so hot I thought my skin might slide right off. Breathing was suffocating. A damp patch was spreading where Laurel's butt met my hip; might be sweat, might not.

I know I ain't got no neighbours, but you're still too old to be prancing around in your birthday suit.

I took the slip and put Laurel down on the grass to go inside and change. She screamed bloody murder, and I just let her.

Myrtle didn't come out the rest of that afternoon. Even in the shade of the oak the heat pressed down like a flat iron. The ground didn't want it, sent it back in shimmering waves. A faded ginger tom sloped up onto the porch. That got the chickens all fired up, but he just yawned, a quick, sharp-toothed affair, then settled his head between his paws. The poor, oblivious chickens settled down. On a rope strung up between two trees, white sheets sagged.

I lay in the water, only my eyes, nose and mouth above the line. When I closed my eyes I could see my own bright blood, and little spidery veins.

I felt Billy's finger in my ribs.

Janey?

Hmm?

How do we know where the end is?

Of what?

The yard. How do we know where the end of the yard is? How do we know how far we're allowed to go?

For crying out loud. I opened my eyes, sat up a fraction. There was the end of the tub, then the yard, a green glimmer, running down to a little dried-up nothing of a creek. A clutch of twisted trees, then a rise of hill. No fence, no boundary, nothing to say what was Myrtles' yard and what wasn't.

I sank back into the water. *Just stay in the tub. Too hot to move anyway.*

Janey?

What? It was the heat made me snappy.

Where'd Mamma go, again?

Yoo-rup. Least I think that's what she said.

How long you reckon it'll take for them to get to Yoo-rup and come back? Week, maybe?

Probly.

The water was cloudy, shadows creeping east, when the door banged open and out came Myrtle. She grabbed a chicken out the coop and, before the thing could think to squawk, she had its neck wrung. Like she was squeezing out a dishcloth. She plucked it right there on the step, feathers flying round her head like the veil of some mad bride. I felt sorry for that bird. Never saw it coming. But I'd be lying if I said I didn't think it was pretty cool.

The rocker squinked, like there was a tiny creature caught in the runners. *How'd she disappear?* Billy demanded. *Was it magic? A trick? What happened to her?*

Myrtle sniffed. *I don't know about no magic tricks. I do know, it happened a while back, not so very far from here.* She gestured towards the window with the stem of her pipe. *She came from a big family, all boys except'n her, and her mamma, course. Those boys was like a swarm of bees, everywhere, into everything, causin mayhem with they sling shots, like they was above consequence.*

The girl, she used to practice with the sling shot in the yard when nobody was lookin, She was a better shot n any a them ham-fisted, wall-eyed boys. She paused, suddenly miles away. *She taught herself to swim in the creek, would swing on that tyre, jumping off at just the highest point, landing splat! in the deepest part of the water.*

Billy sat up straighter, and I saw an idea that couldn't be let come to the boil start to bubble in his mind. And it was as though as if Myrtle had climbed right inside my head. *Might sound brave to you, but it was plain foolish. Creeks around here, full a all kinds a deadly poisonous creatures.* She counted off on her fingers: *Green-hearted frogs; red-toed lizards; black-toothed water rats.* Billy's thumb fell out of his mouth. It stayed open, a perfect, thumb-sized hole. Myrtle jabbed the pipe at him and smoke drifted sideways. She nodded. *That's right.*

So the girl grew up, helping her mamma in the kitchen, watching the boys doing all the things she could better n them, and twice as fast, while she was peggin up their drawers, forkin pie crusts, and lookin after the little ones.

Uncle Joe says girls is only good for kissin and ...Myrtle's glare stopped Billy before I needed to.

Her daddy loved her the way most men love the one girl in the house. Without really knowing who she was, like all girls and women were the same. But he did love her. Guess he must have been destroyed when she disappeared like that.

Every night the girl would walk to the creek, no further, and back home again. There, and back. There, and back, every night. That was as far as she was allowed to go. Myrtle closed her eyes and fell silent. The tops of my thighs were slippery with sweat, the creases in my elbows too. Laurel was snoring a bit. Just when I thought Myrtle had fallen asleep, she leaned forward.

Opposite side of the creek stood a redwood tree, so tall you could see it from the next county. So tall, you could spend your whole life looking up and still never see the top. One night, when she was a bit older than you Janey, I reckon, the girl got to the creek. It was summer, the creek no higher than her ankle-bone. She splashed straight through. Don't ask me why. Maybe it was the heat, or the big tawny moon. But something urged her through that water and up to that tree.

There was a slit in the bark of that tree, just big enough for a girl to slip through. It was cool inside, green moss, soft and cushioney. She lay down, just a minute. Nobody's laid eyes on her since.

But what happened? What happened to the disappeared girl?

Exactly that. She disappeared. They was out at dawn with flashlights and dawgs, police and farmers with they pitchforks, but they never did find her out.

This a true-story? Or a book-story? I wanted to know.

Billy tutted and looked at me that way, like I don't know anything even though I'm four years older than him and know plenty.

Course it ain't true! Girls don't disappear! They'd find her eventually, even if she was just dead, they'd find her.

Myrtle did a mouth-shrug.

Well. They looked insida that tree. Weren't nothin there but moss and twigs and birds feathers. She was never seen again.

They never could find her?

No, Billy, they could not. Maybe they wasn't looking right. Some folks told of seeing a girl, stealing eggs outta they hen houses, pies that was cooling on the sill, getting everybody all stirred up about nothin. So, seems like she did just disappear.

A candle died in a draught. Myrtle was silent a while. *Now, Billy, you tell me, how far do you think you is allowed to go?* But, thing is, she was looking right at me when she said it.

First came the wind, then the rain. Billy was across the foot of the bed, arms flung above his head, hair sweat-slicked. Laurel was squirming in her sleep, little body pressed right up against me. Even my butt was sweating. When I closed my eyes I smelled the fresh air in the cool sheets.

It was the breeze, the sweet breeze that carried her across that creek. The cool water kissed her ankles and as she walked across the parched earth a carpet of fresh green grass sprung up before her. And the breeze had a scent, sugary, yeasty, and she was full of a longing, sharp and strange. And then the breeze was alive, it was flashing red and green and orange, a blizzard of butterflies, each exactly the same as the other, but they swarmed quickly away, leaving only one, a huge radiant purple queen, with a twist of copper hair, and a golden, jewel-encrusted crown. She looked at Janey then winked, flitting off towards the giant redwood tree.

Janey slipped in through the gap, and was amazed to see how huge the tree was inside, big enough for her to lie down and completely stretch out, all the way to the limits of herself. But the butterfly frowned and shook her head no! Janey wanted to stay there, to lie in the tall cool shade of the tree, but the butterfly opened a door in the side of the tree and pushed Janey out, and Janey was amazed to find herself on the shore of a vast and frenzied sea. A hot, wild wind whipped her hair across her face. Lashed to a palm tree was a small sailing boat, bobbing and thrashing in the furious water. Janey looked behind her. The door in the side of the tree was still there, open. Ahead lay the horizon, taut as tripwire.

The boat was tied to the tree in a series of complicated knots, which she was able to negotiate with ease. She looked once more at the redwood tree, and the farm beyond, neat quilted fields replicating themselves over and over, then climbed aboard and picked up the oars. The butterfly hovered near her shoulder. As she rowed it grew cooler and a sudden rain fell, landing on the sails with a sound like popping corn.

Myrtle was making pancakes. I sat up and stretched, peeled myself away from Laurel and Billy, leaving them stranded in the bed.

Jeez, girl, make some noise when you come into a room. Creeping about like a ghost. You sleep ok?

Never better. Had the strangest dream.

That so? She poured a spoonful of batter into the pan and waited for it to bubble.

Uh-huh.

It's the heat. Makes people crazy.

I went to the sink to splash water on my face.

Woah. It all looks so different. The grass was green and springy-looking, the creek running like a racehorse, glinting in the sunlight. I cracked the window open and the air rushing in was cool, fresh.

Myrtle smiled, flipping the blistered pancake. *Yup. There's a change in the air.*

Laurel whimpered. I turned to go to her. Myrtle put her hand on my arm. *Leave her be. Maybe she's dreaming too.*

65

JENNIFER BAILEY

Expiating Irene

I've killed my mother but then I'm saddled with the body, a thing that's strapped to my back. Stooped by the corpse's weight, I hunt for a place to hide it. Someone is weeping but it's not me. No way.

That was my dream the first night. I always dream a lot in strange beds.

My mother's house is chaotic, over-heated, raising a general stink of minimal cleaning. It's set in a row of small brick semis; low ceilings, thin walls, PVC windows, slate roofs shiny with wet, squeezed front gardens, some tended, my mother's with flourishing dandelions and islands of mud in the churned grass. And that's it, that's all there is. The road leads downhill to a village. I'd noticed a small Spar supermarket, pub, café, church. The sky is filthy, birds get flung by the wind, the rain is pitiless.

'Drink, Chickie?'

My mother stands at the far end of her narrow kitchen, holding an industrial size bottle of sherry. I'm sitting at the flap of a folding kitchen table and without considering, I nod. The sherry tastes like sweetened cough syrup and I push it away, run a glass of water to clear my mouth. After swigging her own, my mother finishes mine. They've told me she's a drinker but I've yet to find out what that entails.

So here she is, my mother, making the most of her cheap sad-sack alcohol. Behind her, the window frames a field that rises and vanishes into low cloud, transforming the furthest sheep into ghosts of themselves. Somewhere out there is the motorway, which I exited too soon and so had to navigate a web of roads. I stopped the car, mistaking the headless body for a dog but it was a spread-eagled fox, fur deadened by rain and mud. Its head tilted snarlingly in the roadside ditch, bounced there perhaps by a heavy or fast-moving vehicle. Or dragged from the body by another animal that might have gnawed at the bloody severance. I crouched close to the snout, seeing how the fox's amber eyes still held a memory of life. A blue-backed beetle trekked the grass stems, water gibbered in the ditch, the darker shapes of fells were held in mist.

This isn't my landscape. It belongs to my mother who's moving now like a human crab, legs scissoring sideways to manoeuvre her narrow

66

kitchen, arms waving, and eyes that might be on stalks for all their eager swivelling.

She tugs on my arm, face flushed with excitement.

'Come upstairs Chickie, I want to show you what I'm making.'

I follow her. Chickie was a neglected child. I've already noticed a framed photo of her aged about twelve, hugging Geoff the marmalade cat. His luxurious tail partly obscures her face. I've been Christine for fifteen years, seeing my mother on brief occasions, but there's no precedent for this open-ended visit. I was talked into coming, and if there's another reason, I don't know where I'd find it.

She leads me into a room at the front of the house. It's unfurnished except for a large table and two upright chairs. On the table is a sewing machine, a jumble of flecked grey woollen material cut into shapes, as well as scissors, pins, crumpled tissue paper. There's more material on the floor. My mother holds out a sewing pattern envelope, which shows the drawing of a woman, nineteen fifties style, modelling a suit; short jacket and box-pleated skirt.

'Look Chickie, I'm doing the skirt. The jacket is a bit beyond me. It was going to be a surprise but I'll need to measure you to get the fit right.'

She's standing too close. I can feel the heat coming off her creased cleavage, the fleshy slabs of her arms, the constraint she's exercising so as not to touch.

The material resembles carpet underlay. I'm wearing black jeans, T shirt and loose V neck sweater. Trainers.

I back away from her.

'Listen, can you stick to Christine? And I'll call you Irene.'

I escape to the window, notice a sign stuck into the opposite hedge. It's decorated with crudely drawn cakes and sandwiches, surrounding ornate lettering: *Meg's home-made food – left past the church – you can't miss it!* A gang of shouting boys pass on bikes. One tosses a can.

'But I'm your mother.'

I don't move. We're silent for a while. Then she says,

'You don't like it.'

Where to begin? 'No.'

Silenced, my mother sags in on herself. Rejection is expected. Undeserved of course, but unavoidable. She folds away the material. I tell her to make the skirt for herself, that with new shoes and blouse she'll look terrific. I've no idea what I'm talking about, but it helps with the panic of getting too close to the sadness of her life. She doesn't respond.

For dinner we have white fish and potato mashed together and crisped under the grill, with frozen peas, then rice pudding. My mother says it was my favourite food as a child. She drinks a bottle of sweet white wine; I stick to water. Later, while it's still light, I stand under the back door porch and light a cigarette. The rain is steady, quiet enough to be part of the air, nearly invisible, with a feral earthy smell. A bird whistles, something long drawn out as if signalling.

I stay downstairs while my mother gets ready for bed. She'd kissed me goodnight, fingers round my arms in a tight clutch while she touched her loose cheeks and lips to mine. She smelled of booze and face powder.

I'm in the sitting room and can hear her moving overhead. Twice she's called down, 'Chickie, I've finished in the bathroom,' and I've ignored her. So she comes down again, wearing a nylon knee-length nightdress.

'Go to bed,' I tell her.

I'd kill to be left alone but of course it's not an option.

She's prepared the spare bedroom which is small with a camp bed so narrow I bang my elbows and knees on its metal frame. She wakes me from my murderous dream by flushing the toilet. I'm hot, the window is locked shut, so I throw back the duvet, listening to water filling the toilet cistern. When milky light seeps through the curtains, I cover myself and slide back into sleep, feeling how deep I'm going, how it will last as long as my body needs.

Nothing wakes me up; rather it's a slow rise from a dream about Soames, which is all I can remember. Soames is a photographer who specialises in weddings, portraits of children, of people who want to illustrate their dating website, of anniversary couples. In Soames's photographs, the world is always happy, which is why he's stopped taking them of me.

Late morning, after I've cleared the downstairs room of glasses, mugs, plates and bottles, I hoover Irene's rug which I tamp down with my foot against the suction. The pile rises, giving up crumbs, dark dried mud, lost slivers of sewing thread, scraps of paper. When I change direction, the weave is smoothed, its synthetic fibre glossed by lemony sunlight that throws into relief surfaces furred with dust. I recognise a jug from the old house that Irene sold after my father died, youngish, from a heart attack.

She comes to stand in my line of sight.

'I can do that myself. You're not here to clean the place.'

She folds her arms, waggles her head to mimic a parent's telling-off.

I've noticed grime on the underside of saucers and plates, but switch off the hoover. The sun has given me a boost and I offer to take her for a drive. She agrees but is hesitant and nervy, takes her time choosing a blue polyester jacket and lacing her brogues. Her flesh has outgrown the jacket and in her stoutness, in the melted wax-like sag of her chin I could've passed her unrecognised. She claims she's forgotten something and goes to the kitchen. I wait in the hall and hear the sucking thwack of the sherry bottle cork, wondering how many glasses she'll need to calm herself, and why she needs to be calmed in the first place.

I drive us along narrow roads between blossoming hedges and wind-whipped trees; through villages that combine the usual picturesque with outlying new builds like Irene's. I turn randomly at junctions, expecting her to direct, but she's silent, the only sound her puffing breaths. She holds the edge of her seat, shoulders tense and square. Whenever possible, I steer the car uphill, climbing for the views. We pass occasional shabby houses alongside lines of washing, scattered daffodils and muddied cars. I notice a barn converted to polished stone and narrow churchy windows.

All this thins, and we reach uplands where the car thrums across cattle grids and tracks veer from the road and disappear into higher fell slopes. I pull into a parking space and open my door. The wind sings. Irene refuses to move and I leave her for the nearest track, promising that I won't go far.

I feel boxed in by these fells. The track curves then climbs steeply. I push myself to walk quickly, enduring the burn in my lungs and limbs, and then when it feels right, when there's enough distance from the car, I perch on a stone. The valley bottom spreads, bowl-shaped. Villages cluster. Sheep wander and stare near at hand. There's a stream to my left racketing loudly over and between the tumbled rocks. Clouds drift, making shadows across the slopes. Out of habit I take out my phone, amazed to see there's reception. Soames has sent a message:

I'm missing you too much. Work allows so I'll train it up there, arrival 12.03 tomorrow.

He's added twelve kisses. I climb down to the car, not bothering to reply. Soames will come whatever I write.

We share a flat that's chilly because the radiators don't work properly and neglected sash windows are rattled by passing heavy traffic. I've painted the bedroom, sitting room/kitchenette and bathroom, put up shelves and blinds, because that's the kind of thing I like to do. Opposite the sitting room window is a large gilt-framed mirror I found in a skip. It turns the outside world into a distant miniature.

69

There's a brown stain above the sofa where the coffee cup I was aiming at Soames's head exploded on the wall when he ducked. I struggle with his chirpy remarks that make light of my complaints, his habit of tucking me up at night and moving my slippers so I don't trip over them.

I mean, surely love, or hatred or lust or despair, all that stuff, should be implied. It's too heavy and thick, it needs to come at you on a slant. But Soames is sentimental so I can't explain but have to stick to facile explanations of the downbeat variety, such as, we aren't suited, and I'm no good at relationships. I said I didn't know how long I would stay with my mother, and he just tilted his head to the side, eyebrows raised. It occurs to me now that Soames hadn't believed me. It was just another of my outbursts he thrived on, like I was the manure to his sapling.

Irene is crouched alongside the car, arms round her knees. She looks terrified.

'What?' I shout, pulling her up, 'what's happened?'

She's hysterical.

'I thought you'd left me or you'd been attacked or kidnapped and I don't know where I am.'

The wind takes her words and turns them into terrible accusations.

'Why in God's name would I leave you?'

Her fear feels stupid, unwarranted. Touching her is an ordeal but I help her into the car, thinking to retrace our route, but Irene directs me till the road narrows to a car's width and cuts across a steep expanse of heathered fell-side. She tells me to stop.

'Stop!' she yells. 'Stop now. Here.'

She throws herself out of the car, takes a few steps into the heather, loses balance and sits. I smoke a cigarette. There's a large stone farmhouse below us, and outbuildings with corrugated roofs. Beyond, a tractor crosses a field and the grind of its engine swells and fades. Irene stirs, speaks, but the wind takes her words.

'What?'

This time she shouts. 'I grew up down there.'

Questioning her, it's as if I'm forcing her to confess to some ancient wrongdoing. She won't answer me; bends over her raised knees and glares up at me.

'Get me up, let's go home and out of this damned cold.'

I've long been told all this but the telling was casual, dismissive, without detail. Maybe I hadn't believed any of it.

I don't mention Soames until evening when we've walked down to the pub, her arm linked with mine for fear of falling, she says. It's in the pub I realise she's no anonymous recluse; the barman, a couple with the air of a good night out, an overdressed woman clearing tables, a man against the bar, all of them greeting her with surprised celebration that she's out of the house. Irene pushes me forward but all I get are polite nods, cool distant smiles.

She gulps her gin and tonic.

'It's not personal. I don't go out and being on my own, they think I'm neglected. Abandoned. They think.'

I won't be provoked.

'What, never?'

'Not if I can help it. Look what happened earlier; nowhere is safe. I wouldn't be surprised if those fells were crawling with crazy people, the types who build makeshift shelters, take drugs and for all I know carry guns. Besides, it's easy to get lost.'

'But you know this area.'

'That was before the motorway, before visitors. Tourists.' She drinks thirstily. 'I was told that during the War, signposts were taken down, so anyone asking for directions was a spy. Besides, there was a prisoner of war camp up Grizedale.'

'You're agoraphobic,' I say to stop her flow but she turns down her mouth, unimpressed.

'If you like.'

The overdressed woman comes with another gin and takes away Irene's empty glass.

'Compliments of Larry.'

A man with an overheated face raises his beer mug. Irene returns the gesture.

'How d'you know all these people if you never go out?'

'I told you. I grew up round here. It's like the time I lived away never happened.'

Which includes the first fifteen years of my life.

People brush by our table, even some of the lads on their way to getting drunk, and my mother performs as a well-liked old woman who shows with her gaiety how deserving she is.

I feel let off the hook, and so tell her about Soames' visit.

He's pliant is Soames. He sways and rustles round people, gives them the shelter of his attention. He can listen indefinitely, his eyes holding a direct gaze; his wide smile shows sexy incisors, he has large hands that soothe. I watch him work precision photographic equipment; how his long fingers manipulate delicate adjustments. His voice is yappy though, a legacy of public schooling, overlaid with a London twang.

My mother flirts. Her smile is brilliant, her laughter free-ranging. She acts like she's forgotten who he is, why he's here, and treats him like a favoured acolyte, dispensing food, mugs of tea and alcohol as if they're a series of treats. Soames isn't embarrassed. He plays up his role.

'Were there really two staircases in the house where you grew up?'

'Two staircases.' My mother nods solemnly. She's drinking red wine. 'The one we mostly used was narrow and curved upstairs from the kitchen. The other you saw as soon as you walked through the front door.'

I leave them to it and wash the underside of her crockery, clean the cutlery, drawers and cupboards.

Soames comes to find me. Irene has gone to bed; he wants to know where he'll sleep.

'Put sofa cushions on the front room floor. It'll be cooler there, cleaner as well, less whiffy.'

'I like her. She told me about your father.'

I shake my head, knowing these stories from old, the mournful relish of her litanies; 'I could've been a professional singer' and 'if only' in the telling of my father's studied indifference, alternating with his criticisms; her loneliness, frustrations. And so on and on.

I turn back to the sink. Soames presses me from behind, puts his arms round my waist.

'What is it?' he murmurs and I push him away.

'Soames' I say carefully, 'I'm not coming back.'

'You're staying here?'

He's incredulous and then, because I don't reply, we separate, him to arrange the sofa cushions, me to get bedding. I heap our jackets over the only blanket I've been able to find, and he kisses me. I resist his attempts to pull me onto the cushions.

'I'll stay another day, another night; OK?' and he's gazing at me, holding my face at different angles, as if looking for something that might catch the light. Then he kisses me again. I don't argue.

Moonlight penetrates the curtains. It's four fifteen and I feel alert as if something is about to happen, something urgent, so I pull on socks, boots, sweater and jacket over T shirt and knickers. These rapid movements shift the air. I smell gamey. Downstairs and passing Soames' door, I hear his whistling breaths, then I'm out of the house. Turning away from the village, I break into a jog, exhilarated by silence, by the sky jazzed with stars and my speed in a nowhere direction. The moon is nearly full, and the fells and fields reflect its ashy light. I stop next to a gate. Something screams, there's a clatter of wings to my left where a small thicket blends to make a formless mass. I climb the gate and continue running, stumbling sometimes over uneven quaggy grass, with an energy that feels unstoppable, except I reach a barrier. It's a broad dense hedge of brambles. Thorny branches prick against the lightening sky. The moon has set.

We're sitting in the back garden which is mostly flagged patio with an apron of balding lawn, Irene in a chair I've brought outside, me and Soames on the blanket he slept under. Surrounding us are jumbled tea things, full and empty beer bottles, plates, a plastic ketchup dispenser. The sun is warm enough and I'm in and out of a doze, while Irene chatters. Her voice pushes me back into the doze.

I'm dreaming her words.

'There were blue cats with bright orange eyes, feral, they'd come into the kitchen for scraps, quick, then out again, claws tearing on stone flags, keeping mostly to the barn and the rats.'

Soames's encouraging murmurs.

'My father made me a rope swing, tied it to a beam in the hay loft and I'd drift through columns of light that fell between gaps in the roof, the dust jumping and threading around me.'

I see it.

Then,

'I loved Jack. His kennel by the back gate was big enough for sleeping and eating though when it was empty he'd throw out his bowl. He'd a savage-sounding bark but a soft throaty whine when I came to stroke him.'

Then Soames, 'wait, just give me a moment.'

She's humming quietly, and I keep my eyes closed. He returns. It's cool when a cloud covers the sun but I'm relaxed.

'What else?' he asks, and I hear him busying.

'Collecting bilberries on the fells. Lambing, one in a box by the Aga and I'd feed it from a bottle. Also we had three hen houses. I'd rattle a bucket and they'd run, flowing towards me while I scattered the grain. There was never a sight like that.'

Soames' keenness has turned her voice stagey. She's inventing. If there was ever any truth in this Never Land shite, it's been worn away by time.

I sit up, slitting my eyes against the light. Soames is holding his camera, fingers round the lens, turning, clicking, turning, clicking. He kneels, hunched forward.

'Keep talking,' he urges Irene, 'more, give me more.'

'I had the loveliest voice. My father accompanied me on the piano.'

She sits upright in her chair, an inward gaze, seeing it all, while Soames moves round her, camera to his face, finding the angles.

In six weeks and three days Irene will die after a brief stay in hospital. She'll not be alone though I won't recognise the names.

I'll be glad I made this visit.

And I'll be glad she's dead.

I get up and taking my time, walk into the house. My eyes have trouble adjusting. I look back out at them. Soames crouches over his camera screen, Irene sings, her voice growly and uncertain.

Some enchanted evening

You may see a stranger, you may see a stranger

Across a crowded room

Her head is tipped, face to the sky. She lifts her arms from the chair a little and beats out a rhythm. I think I like her just then. I think, this is how she wanted to have lived. And listen, just listen to how she's held onto that.

SALLY FRANICEVICH

Uncle Frank's Turkeys

'If he presents himself at the door like he did last time,' says Bubs, 'I'm going to say something to him. I'm going to say, '"for goodness *sake* Frank, put some proper clothes on! Get dressed properly before you come to the door to greet me!"'

Francine unloads the caramel slice and cheese and tomato sandwiches. She puts the tray on the spare chair next to them and hands a sandwich to her grandmother. 'Poor old Frank,' she says.

'Poor old Frank?' says Bubs, 'Poor old Bruno you mean! All the cooking! All the washing! Frank stuck in bed like someone's broken both his legs with a mallet.' She snaps open her handbag and takes out a hanky. 'Him and his *brandy*. Him and his blimmin' *turkeys*.' She shakes the hanky free from its ironed creases.

'Has he found them? The turkeys? Have they come back?'

'Lenny Pedersen from over-the-back rang Bruno. Said the turkeys had ended up over at his place. Said they were all *over* the show. What's poor Bruno going to do about it? Run over to Lenny's with a fishing net? They're scattered all over the show now,' says Bubs, 'all *over* the blimmin' show. Those turkeys!' The bobble-catch of her bag claps shut with the sound of cracking bone.

'He should have seen to them when they were still young,' Francine says, and then thinks, *listen to me: 'seen to them,' as if I know anything about it. As if I could kill anything.*

'Frank said he didn't want to be a *murderer*. He did the first one all right then skittered back into the kitchen covered in poop and blood and muck crying like a nutcase. Said he couldn't stand it. Said they were his *friends*. Said he'd let them all out of the pen to run *free*.'

'Oh poor Uncle Frank!'

'Nothing *poor* about him! He left his dirty poopy clothes all over the floor for Bruno to clean up and went to bed with a nice big bottle of brandy. A nice big bottle.'

'And poor old Bruno. Poor old both of them.'

Bubs huffs. She looks up between the pine trees where the view of the hills to the north is clear.

Francine sees her look and understands: poor old Bubs too! Dragging herself all the way up north to the Old Place. Coming all this way to visit her brothers when she could have stayed at home with her feet up on the flower-patterned footstool. Could be at home right this minute, listening to the song of the dishwasher, listening to the washing machine on its spin cycle, listening to all the sweet singing of modern white-ware. Resting her eyes on the Young and The Whatsit on the television, a teabag sitting in the cup and a shop-bought biscuit in the saucer.

When they finish their lunch, Bubs and Francine, grandmother and grand daughter, climb back into Francine's car and drive deeper into the countryside.

Back country, Francine thinks and wonders why the thought chills her and sends her eyes swiveling around for escape.

After an hour or so they arrive at the river, or the river arrives at them: sneaks up beside them like a nasty kid to hiss in their ears.

'God it's high today!'

'Gives me the creeps,' says Bubs, 'Horrible thing. Brown as muck.'

Francine knows Bubs never liked living in the country, hated being on the farm when she was young. Maybe Uncle Frank had always hated it too? But Frank was the eldest son and he'd inherited everything: the stock, the land, the self-regarding swagger, the papers from the solicitor's office with the rose-pink stamp; everything was Frank's, whether he wanted it or not.

No one could remember exactly when Frank's crying had started. It might have been when he'd been gored by the bull. Maybe that had been the turning point? It sounded right. A goring by a bull seemed like the kind of thing that would do that to you, but no one could remember for sure.

The first time anyone noticed things changing was the business with the bobby calves. Well, Francine thought, who could stop themselves from loving a pink-snouted bobby-calf? Not Uncle Frank! Not when it mewed for its mummy from inside the gate-pen. One day, Frank suddenly flung open the wire front of the dreadful pen and let the little calves bound out across the grass to the roaring bellowing cows who dripped and cried and called out for them.

That had been years ago, but Francine remembers the phone call. Uncle Bruno's shouts audible at the other end of the phone line. Bubs saying, 'Oh for goodness sake!' and, 'you wouldn't read about it!'

As the road peels away from the river it takes them under the mountain. They fall silent as the Old Place pulls them forward. At last they arrive.

'God!' says Bubs, 'Here we are!'

Francine gets out of the car with the engine still running and walks over to pull the long gate open. They drive through and then stop again so she can get out and close it behind them.

Ok, here we go, she thinks.

The car bounds over the bumps and valleys of the driveway. They hear the dogs scream and see Bruno – dear darling Bruno – heave the Top Gate back for them.

'That's not Bruno is it?' says Bubs, high up in her seat. 'Is it? By God it is! It's Bruno! He's opening the Top Gate for us! Is he waving?' Her strong old arm goes out the car window to wave back. It's going to be all right, says the wave. Here I am. I'm home.

When they walk up to the front steps Uncle Frank throws open the door to greet them. 'Thank God you've arrived!' he says, tremulous and teary, kissing them. He is dressed in his long johns.

'For goodness sake Frank,' says Bubs, just as she rehearsed at the café, 'go and put some proper clothes on!' But to make up for her tone and to make up for not thanking God for her arrival, she follows him down the hallway to say, 'I've bought you a new shirt all the way from Wellington,' she says, 'from Hallenstein's'.

Francine hears thumps on the porch and Uncle Bruno comes back from the heavy business of lacing the gate shut and cursing the dogs.

'Halloh! Halloh!'

He grips Francine hard for a kiss.

'You scooted past me Missus,' he calls down the hallway to Bubs, 'I was up at the Top Gate, looking to hitch a lift to the house,'and then he adds in the old language, so Francine can't understand, though surprisingly, here in this house, she finds she can, '*He's been like that for weeks. It's the brandy. Always the brandy.*'

'*Sramota*,' says Bubs walking back into the room, 'shame', but her look is of expectation fulfilled.

'I'll make us some tea, Missus.'

To help Bruno get the tea ready, Francine opens the cupboard against the kitchen wall and picks out cups and saucers. The swell of the cups slide under her thumb. There is no smart city detergent here, just yellow soap in a wire holder to rattle in the dishwater. Something clings to the dishes that the soap can't remove. *Don't think about it*, Francine tells herself. She tries to keep her precious city stomach to herself, pushes away thought of mutton fat and old butter.

They sit around the big table to drink their tea.

'Well Missus! Well!' Bruno says to Bubs, smiling.

With Bruno everything has its own rhythm, rounded out by the bounce of something funny, something he heard long ago maybe, a rhyme or a joke. It might only be there in the mark of its beat on his words. Bubs might catch the whiff of an old family story. Francine might hear funniness she can't put her finger on.

'Well Missus, well!'

Bubs turns the teapot, once, twice, three times, and pours the tea. She married and left this place when she was young, so young that being called 'Missus' was still a joke and a surprise. 'Missus' when she was still seventeen! 'Missus' when maybe they thought she would stay on here forever, cooking and washing and cleaning and tending to the lot of them. Caught here forever like a beast stuck in a drain.

Bruno stirs his cup in celebration at their arrival. How Francine loves him and how she loves to hear him stir his tea! Bang bang bang on the side of his cup,

Here you are

And

Here I am

And

Here we are Together again!

And then: Tonk! Tonk! TONK! As he hits the spoon on the edge of the cup to shake off the last crumb of tea before he slots it back in his saucer. CLACK! He could be setting off fireworks or blowing out candles or popping champagne corks. *Clacketty-clack!*

As they drink their tea, Frank comes back down the hallway. He has his new shirt from Hallensteins on now, still creased from its packet and tucked tightly into his trousers. Now you can see what he'd once been: a man with the wire hands of a back-country farmer, sure about everything he needed to be sure about. A man who could build the world, fence by fence, just let him jump in the blimmin' truck and get on with it! No need, back in those days, to stay in bed all day with his brandy. No need, back then, to cry about the turkey chicks and the baby calves. He'd built this farm up from more or less nothing hadn't he? Paid the haymakers with the layers he peeled off his dog-roll of hundred dollar notes? Bronco-ed his Mercedes sedan across the paddocks, stock-feed in a waving tower on the back seat. A rich bugger, with a rich bugger's team of truck-slapping, gear-heaving, surf-casting mates to bark and mutter and shout out to.

And now it has come to this: all day in bed and then up half the night in front of the bed-sized TV with only his brandy and Bruno, Bruno who loves and hates him. Bruno, who made his tucker every day and stripped down his bed on Saturdays, who started up the lappetty-lap old washing machine and hung his sheets up in the sun. No sisters living with them now. Mum dead. Never any wives. Just the two of them. *Lapetty-lap*.

'I'll just have a bittuva look,' says Frank. He walks past Bubs, Francine and Bruno as they drink their tea at the table and unhooks a pair of binoculars from underneath the fountain of coats and hats and plastic bags on the hook behind the door.

Bruno and Bubs exchange looks.

After the grief with the bobby calves Frank changed from dairying to fattening beef cattle. No bobby calves, no crying cow-mummies. It worked for a while. The cattle beasts who arrived on the truck were already half-grown and you could avoid loving them if you put your mind to it. But still it was no good. Even from among the big cattle beasts, Frank made a pet, an enormous steer he had loved since it arrived on the truck as a rough-headed youngster. Frank called it '*Malo*'. Little One.

Frank scans the Home Paddock with his binoculars.

'His turkeys have taken off again,' Bruno mutters in a voice low enough so that Frank will have to pretend not to hear him, 'they've gone *flatting*.'

Francine guffaws from her chair by the chest freezer. Bruno stays as deadpan as a stage comedian.

'Good job!' says Bubs. 'I'm sick of hearing about those blasted turkeys!' she sucks her tea in the special way she does when she's here at the Old Place, keeping the worst of the tea-heat away from her face with a long lip-funnel and a hefty intake of breath. It is a sign of sister-and-brotherhood, this slurping. She would never have slurped her tea like this at the café.

While they sit at the table and watch Frank with his binoculars. Bubs gives her cup of tea another stir, matching Bruno meaningfully: clacketty-clack CLACK.

'Those blinking turkeys!' she says.

'Those blinking turkeys alright Missus! Tell me about it!'

When their tea is finished and Francine has carried the cups and saucers back to the sink, they unhook plastic bags from behind the door and go outside. The day is ripe with sun and there are fallen walnuts to collect from behind the chook house.

'No chook-poopy ones for me,' says Bubs.

Francine is careful to only pick the green walnuts from the grass at the foot of the trees, but even these are eaten away and black on their undersides, surprising her with their broken-up bellies when their tops had gleamed and looked so whole in the sun.

'Natural antibiotics in chook poop,' Bruno says as he bends to fit under the stinking rim of the chook run. 'Nothing wrong with them Missus. Best place to get them.'

He reappears with his hands full of clean nuts.

This is how it is here, Francine thinks, the dirtiest, most rotten things always the best. Fish-gut fertilizer for the jeweled mandarin trees, the ugly tucker-bucket for the sweetest licky-est dog, muck and mess always the best for everything.

When their bags of walnuts are full, Bubs hooks back the steel cord and opens the corrugated iron gate to the orchard.

There, around the corner, is Little One. He's stomped around the far side of the house and pushed himself between the side of the old garage, and Bruno's blue Morris and here he is, eating the leaves off Bruno's specially grafted apple trees.

'Shoo you blasted thing!'Bruno shouts. 'Shoo!'He marches across the hoof-marked mud waving his arms. 'Frank's *pet*,' he says, 'Frank's blasted *pet*! Shoo!'

Frank, still on the other side of the house and scanning the world with his binoculars, must have heard Bruno's shout because he begins his call, '*Malo! Malo! Malo!*' in the lowing, down-facing tone he uses for the animals. '*Malo!*'

The beast pauses in its chomping for a moment then shuffles off towards Frank's voice, bending its head in readiness for Frank's rub on the boney ridge between its ears.

'*Malo! Malo!*' they hear Frank singing out of sight.

'Blasted thing!' Bruno shouts after it.

Just along from the chook house, the fig trees seethe with wax eyes. The little birds look just like the figs, russet and leaf-coloured and in the shape of buxom tears. Each tree is a wriggling city of bird-fruit. Francine looks up at them and wonders how it can be, that in spite of appearances, in spite of the match in shape and colour, the fruit and the birds weren't made for each other at all. The wax-eyes, fitting and camouflaged as they are, aren't any more native to the land around them than the trees. They had introduced themselves, finding their own tiny way here from some place else and then burrowing into the warp and weft of the place until they were perfectly matched to the leaves and the fruit on the trees.

'A blimmin' racket and a half,' says Bubs of the excited birds. She reaches up and pulls a fig-laden branch towards her. All the ripe figs are bird-hollowed and the others, nowhere near ripe enough. 'Nothing worse than a green fig.'

Francine finds a fig ripe enough for Bub's taste that the birds haven't already got to and hands it over. Bubs accepts it, suspiciously at first, and then sucks out a bite.

'Lovely and sweet,' she said, 'want some?'
Here you are
And
Here I am
And
Here were are
Together again!

Despite the joy of seeing Bruno, despite the ripe fig and the bag of walnuts, Bubs is bleak, her face set in bleakness. The Old Place weighs her down like this every time. There's Frank to worry about: his drinking and his staying in bed, and then there's the kitchen calling her name as it always does. The whole house is full of dust that doesn't bear looking at, memories that don't bear thinking about and no matter how hard she cleans, everything will be just as bad the next time she comes, the house would be just as rotten with things that should have been cleaned up and done away with long ago: half-scraped roasting pans, the dog-tucker bucket pulling flies, a stovetop pot holding God-only-knows. Fly papers and butter wrappers, newspaper and plastic bags, a tin of olive oil high as a chair; all left in places no woman, no proper woman, would ever allow.

'Long day,' says Francine.

'I'll say,' says Bubs.

They put the bags of walnuts down on the table. Bubs sighs and ties on the apron that has sat in the drawer, ironed and ready, since her last visit. The apron string goes twice around her skinny middle.

Relieved of his usual duties, Bruno has set out a leg of mutton to greet her. A roast. Bubs will put on a roast. Bruno and Frank are her brothers and you put on a roast for your brothers, even when it isn't your home anymore, even when it's a farmhouse you left a thousand-and-one years ago, the minute you found your marriage-legs and hitched up your skirt to run.

81

Oh she had run!

'Poor old Bruno,' she says, 'he does his best. He can't be expected.'

Bubs doesn't really expect Bruno to understand the language of the kitchen. Not in its grammatical and proper form. Not even Francine, woman though she is, can be trusted with it; though she stands at the bench in the ready-to-help position, all misted-up glasses and long wrists. Bubs pushes her away, almost gently.

'I'll do this,' she says, 'you go and sit down.'

Francine accepts the push. She knows in her heart that Bubs means to save her from the kitchen-fate, to fight her away from the stove and the bench, to shoo her all the way back to the city where a woman can have cheese on toast for tea and catch a bus into town any time she likes, where she can go a full lifetime without once scrubbing out a dog-tucker bucket.

Unwanted in the kitchen, Francine drifts outside again. From the front of the house, the view of the hills is broken by a row of sheds and old cars and the jagged wings of macrocarpa trees. Wire-netting has unfurled to the size of a train tunnel, an old copper, still singing with shouts, sits by the rib cage of a cart, grass up through it like wheat, pie-cut wheels stacked beside it long ago.

This is what happens without women, Francine thinks, *this mess.* There are no sisters living here anymore, no women left here at all. Like Bubs they had run early and far and to a good safe distance. Now, like Bubs, they lived too far away to come and visit very often.

In the last of the orange sunlight the fig trees still rattle with birds. Francine scans the branches for any ripe and un-bird-hollowed figs. There aren't many, but slowly, she gathers a small handful and carries them, carefully as eggs, around the side of the house to the porch.

Standing beside the porch she looks down to the sunken hammock of the Home Paddock. The Home Paddock is big and broad enough to sweep down to a hollow and then back up again to the edge of the road. Its long curve is wide enough to catch the light as well as the shade of the afternoon.

In the lowest part of the green dip she sees Frank. He's standing knee deep, almost thigh deep, in a sea of bobbing turkeys, a whole world of turkeys, scrabbling and hustling like desperate fans all around him.

'Bubs!' Francine calls out over her shoulder towards the door and the kitchen where Bubs heaves pans and kicks the curling lino. '*Bubba!*' she calls out, '*Dodi ovdje!* Come and look at this!'

She hears the gong of a dropped pan and Bubs comes striding out quickly, rubbing her hands on her apron.

'What the heck...' she stands next to Francine shading her eyes with her hand, taking in the scene. 'You wouldn't read about it,' she says, 'him and his *blimmin' turkeys!*'

Down at the very lowest part of the paddock Frank is throwing corn from a sack at his feet. He bends down to the sack and throws handfuls in big arcs. The grain floats in a shining circle for a moment, and then sinks back down in slow motion to the waiting turkeys. Francine and Bubs watch as the golden rings of corn rise and fall through the air, each circle hovering before it falls down to the passionate, grateful turkeys.

'Hah! Will you look at that!' says Bubs and she laughs. She shouts with laughter and slaps her hands hard down on her apron.

She's happy for Frank, happy to see him content at last, happy to see his golden halo rise and fall around him.

JEREMY GALGUT

The Avalanche

When he had his first fight with Simon, Jake's instinct was to defend. It happened decades ago, when they were still at school, but Jake has convinced himself recently that it was a significant moment. Defence is his first reaction here as well, as the avalanche overtakes them. He falls and realises what is happening, hearing Anna call 'Avalanche!' three times, so he puts his hands over his face.

It creates a small cavity in the snow around his mouth, which means he can breathe more easily then the others, which in turn gives him the strength to push upwards and break through to the surface. He is still unable to get out, because he is in a diagonal position and the snow is packed on top of him, but he can breathe fresh air. He can see the sky which has no colour and in the very corner of his vision one of Simon's skis.

Anna is only just behind Jake, less than three feet at the closest point. She has been at the back because she is the best skier. She is buried no deeper than Jake but her head is two feet beneath the surface and she cannot move. She is in no pain but feels anaesthetized and is aware of the cold without feeling it. Her complete immobility seems to have brought calmness, although in any case she is the member of the group temperamentally most capable of dealing with danger. When she was younger, she did relief work and saw death close up. Aware that the oxygen will get poorer very quickly, she concentrates on the possibilities. She and Jake are both carrying bleepers and there were at least three other groups off-piste when they set out. There is hope.

Jake has thought about the bleepers too, though he is defending himself from thoughts of dying in the way he defends himself from everything, by considering the material. Jake is a writer who works mostly from his imagination. This is one of the few occasions when he could be living the story to be written. He is aware that he is in mortal danger and that there must be more practical and honourable thoughts to be having. He tries to think of Anna, who he supposes must be close by, though he doesn't realise the distance is less than three feet. He wants to get properly caught up in this terrible moment, but the story is on his mind.

Anna doesn't know which way she is facing, but it is not towards Jake. Gerard is twelve feet to her right. If there were no snow they would be staring directly at each other. Gerard grabbed onto a tree, which saved his life as he was being carried down much faster than the others. He is the least experienced skier and Anna has taken the time to train him. He is however the best at making the most of the holiday. His German is good and he has led them into a social scene which they would never have found without him. He is now physically the least damaged but is more sensitive to the pain than the others and he can't help thinking of the cosy boarding house where they are staying, of the immense breakfasts with porridge, eggs, cold meats, strong coffee. If it wasn't so shockingly cold, Gerard would weep.

Simon, who lost that school yard fight in spite of his bravado, is almost upside down. His mother told him when he was young that when falling it is better to allow the body to relax, because that way you won't break your legs. Simon is not fully conscious and is not aware of his mother's or anybody else's words, only of short, flashing dreams. But he did not attempt to resist when the avalanche came. It happened only eleven minutes ago but the rapidly changing dreams are disorientating and he could have been here for hours. He didn't put his hands to his face like Jake, or grab out like Gerard, he just allowed himself to be lanced into the snow, almost head first. He knows that there is snow and that he is in trouble, but he doesn't know he is upside down. There is little space around his face and the excess of carbon dioxide is already worsening the situation. For a few seconds he dreams of Anna.

Jake strains his eyes sideways towards Simon's ski. He can't see enough of it to realise that it is a ski, but it is his only reference point. What would it be like beneath the snow? Dark? He will ask the others. He assumes, rightly as it happens, that he is the only one whose head is above surface. He has tried shouting, but the sounds are tiny and drain away to nothing. When he shouts, he realises how hard it is for his body. The snow is packed tightly around him, as if he is bound up like a mummy.

So he thinks of his story, yet to be recorded. His wife, Anna, has some kind of feeling for the friend Gerard, the man who it is impossible to dislike. And the other, older friend, Simon, has feelings for Anna. Jake is more sure of this, he can see it in Simon's soulful brown eyes when he looks at her. So Jake could be cuckolded twice over. Anna is too good for him, that is the prosaic truth beneath his literary artifice. From the foot of the mountain yesterday afternoon, he watched her descend with such grace, leaving a track like a ribbon. Others watched too. He looks at the ski again, hoping for a movement in a world so silent and still that it could be dead.

Gerard is the only one who is trying to move, though he cannot free himself. He extends his fingers with the desire to touch. Anyone's hand will do. Only Gerard is free of secret passions on this trip and he is the most generous with his feelings. Now he would gladly be the companion of any one of the others, he would help them unconditionally. Although he is so afraid, Gerard manages to take some comfort in the possibility of them being saved and then sitting around a table together, served with bread and wine before the big meal. He moves his fingers again. Anna is nearest, but if they were aware of this it would mean much more to her than to him. Really, anyone's hand will do.

Simon, with his ski clearly protruding from the snow, is their best hope of rescue and survival, even though he is now barely conscious. The last dream was about a plane, it was probably bound for America. It is meant to be the next stage in Simon's life, a posting in America. This is why they are all on holiday together, Simon and his oldest friend Jake. It would be more significant as a goodbye if it was just the two of them, but the presence of Anna has unravelled the meaning. Simon has watched Anna with his worshipful eyes and Jake has watched Simon, wanting his jealousy to be fed. And both men have watched Anna watching Gerard; it becomes dizzying. Jake looks at the ski, still not knowing what it is apart from an object which is not snow or sky.

The thought of America – that it was never really for him – shoots across Simon's mind like a final crackle of electricity which produces sparks and then is extinguished.

Anna concentrates on the bleepers. They are carrying phones as well. She wonders if anyone can reach them. She is sure that she is not the only one buried because she saw bodies somersaulting through the blizzard in front of her as she was thrown along. But they could have been lucky, there could be help on the way right now. They could be so close but she just can't hear. In the silence she wonders if this is punishment. She has spent too much time with Gerard, unable to resist the pleasure of being with a man who can talk and find pleasure in every aspect of the world. A morning walk with him can make her happy in a way as simple as she has known since childhood. Yesterday she had a very clear thought: that if he should reciprocate her feelings, if he were to suddenly announce that he wanted to be with her, she would say yes. Even in the act of thinking, it was a shock to realise what she was willing to do. At the moment she feels no pain, no cold, she doesn't know that her back is broken. She wouldn't want to believe that it could be punishment. Not just for a thought, surely.

Jake thinks that trying to dig himself out could pull him further in, but it is so hard to think with any kind of logic. He knows that an avalanche has something to do with a weakness in the ice-pack. There may be a layer beneath him which will not hold his weight and he will disappear, metres down, suffocating slowly. He begins to panic at the thought of the others, suffocating, waiting for him to save them. He has started to try to move his hands when he sees a shadow near the ski. This seems to be significant. Something must have happened. Then he hears a dog bark and he nearly laughs. The St Bernard with the cask of brandy, he thought that was a myth. He makes himself smile.

Simon is dug out first, because the rescue groups haven't noticed Jake. He tries to shout. Only when one of them nearly steps on him do they see that he is there. He is released very slowly, the men asking every few seconds whether he can move a certain part of the body, whether he is in pain.

'There are others.'

The sound of his own voice, though cracked and high, is a great relief. It feels like life re-starting.

The rescuers are already looking for the other two. They are well equipped and the bleeper allows them to locate Anna. They search in circles around her and Jake watches their grave faces. Gerard will be in her orbit. They locate him and start to dig. Jake is out of the snow now and refuses to be taken away until he has watched the story unfold. He drinks tea and allows himself to be examined by the medic. Gerard is nearly out, Anna is still half buried and is being given oxygen. Two medics are working together and even then they have to radio for advice. Jake turns around and looks at Simon who has been uncovered. His face is pale and his eyes closed, his long eyelashes frosted.

They were ten years old and didn't know how to fight, but in the end Jake managed to get a punch in. Simon's skin was very smooth and Jake's fist hit his eye socket, not very hard but it left a bruise. It still makes him angry now, how he got the blame when it had been a fair fight and in any case it was Simon who had done wrong over the girl. Jake can't get this out of his mind, even as Simon is put onto the stretcher.

He watches the medical team but his eyes are drawn to the horizon. The ground is frozen for miles around and if these acres of ice could be pulled back, the trees and fields would be torn up, leaving a fresh wound on the earth. It would heal differently next time.

A blanket is laid is over his oldest friend, who is then lifted with great gentleness and carried away.

HELENA GREY

Bonxie

A va lay in bed in the little tin house that was bitten to rust by the salt shore air, listening to the waves forever lapping at the grey rocks and the kittiwakes forever mewling like babies. She pulled the layers of duvet and blankets above her shoulders and heard the storage heater click beyond the curtain and thought she should get a cat, or maybe a small dog, for company. But that was for later.

She was spending a lot of time asleep. She, in middle age, had been made redundant from a job she discovered that she didn't much care about. She had been prodded through the meetings and signed all the forms, and then been left with a handful of months' pay in the bank. She slunk away, threadbare.

With one last effort she clamped her teeth on the essence of herself and realised that there was nothing to keep her where she had always been. Her daughters were grown and flown, her friends could live without her, she had no partner and now no job. Frantic and ruthless, she piled her clothes and crockery and ornaments into boxes and gave them away. She put her house up for rent.

'Where will you go? What will you do?' Adam asked her, worried, she thought, more for himself than for her.

She wished he would back off. Shetland, she told him aggressively, a random, distant place that meant nothing to her. And then, when she saw how sad he looked, she felt obliged to give him something to cheer his image of her, so she said, 'I want to write my book there.' He raised his eyebrows and smiled. She hadn't meant to give so much away, hadn't meant to tell him, hadn't, in fact, realised herself that that was what she wanted to do. But now she had said it, it seemed true.

Ava regarded Adam as a comma in her life, or an ellipsis catching an indulgent pause and nothing more. He arrived in her space for a clutch of days at a time, then left without rift to return to his wife and his child. The sex they had was fresh and daring and thoughtful; there was much care between them, but no need. There were moments when she wondered if either of them wanted more, but she felt wise when she drew away from that thought.

Adam had wealth and wore a tailored suit to do the sort of job she didn't understand. He was always generous to her which she found a burden at times. Now he was looking at her seriously. He told her he would find her somewhere to live; he would visit her often; they could spend plenty of time together. She narrowed her eyes, and accepted. It would make her money last longer. And it was sensible, she told herself, now all her reference points were gone.

Adam, maybe for his own reasons, maybe because he did not understand, rented her a house on the north coast of Orkney and not on Shetland after all. It was still far away; it suited her well enough. And so Ava moved into Zanzibar, the tiny corrugated house a handful of yards from the round-pebbled beach at Birsay. From the salt-skinned window of the living room she looked inland and saw dairy cows and beef cattle on the deep green grass, and beyond them the thick walls of the grey-rendered houses that the sensible people owned, the ones who really lived and worked on the island, houses with good insulation and double glazing and front doors that fitted. From the bathroom window she looked across the Sound and saw seals lumbering on the tables of rock, and twice a day she watched the tide pull away from the causeway that led to the longhouses on the Brough. When she lay in the bath she could see the oystercatchers and the herring gulls and the skuas wheeling on the currents.

This three-roomed house, like its name painted on its front door, felt ridiculous, a play house, but she didn't care. With the heavy curtains drawn she could shut out the draughts and the everlasting light of these summer days, and when winter came she would be able to pull them closed over the interminable dark. Now she was here she would be able to indulge in whatever she wanted. And what she wanted was simple. She wanted to walk on the beach. She wanted to read, and write a little. She wanted to speak to no one she didn't care to speak to. And for now she really, truly wanted to be left alone.

She was only mildly surprised at the vehemence with which she thought this.

She had arrived in the middle of a damp afternoon, and it had been damp ever since. The house smelt unloved, unlived in. Grains of sand gritted the wooden floor, the shells of mussel and limpets and barnacled pebbles clustered in the windowsills, a book of short stories was butterflied in a corner of the bathroom. She flicked the heaters on in the living room and the kitchen and the bathroom.

She had not brought much with her. She planned to live minimally, tucked in; she was relishing the prospect of neatness and order. She shuffled around, putting things away, her towels and toothbrush in the bathroom, coffee and wine on the worktop in the kitchen. She wondered if the settee folded out to a bed and knew there would have been a time she would have minded this. She pictured Adam here, him so used to his casual luxury, his legs protruding from a twisted cover, but she knew he would not comment or complain. She was his escape and he indulged himself in her fully.

In the living room there was a cupboard with a panelled door that reached right up to the ceiling. She would stack her clothes and books in there, out of sight and tidy. She slid the door aside; a brocade drape hung heavily over the opening. She lifted it up and found that, instead of shelves, there was a raised mattress and the honey-flower smell of long waxed wood. The sight of the bed, the ticking and buttoning, made her realise how tired she was from the sorting and the packing and the two days of driving. She climbed up and in and slid the door shut and closed the curtains. In the dark and the silence, she fell asleep.

* * *

The next three days she slept deeply and often in the dark of the box bed, sometimes with the door shut completely, often with just the curtain pulled over to shut out the light. She picked at some books, but her concentration was patchy. More often she just lay back and drifted with the sea in her head.

On the fourth day a van pulled up by the gate. She had become so unused to seeing people she felt reluctant to open the door. She peeped through the window first and saw a man hugging a wrap of yellow roses. 'There's no card on these,' he said, handing them over. 'Do you know who they're from?' She began to answer but a large skua dived towards him, feet and beak aimed at his face, and he ran back to his van, shouting, 'Bloody bonxies! They'll be nesting in your garden! You take care now!'

There was no vase for the roses. She snipped the stems short and fitted them inelegantly into a jug. She put them on the small table in the living room; they seemed untidy and intrusive in the house, and were in the way when she ate her tea. But it was good to know Adam was thinking of her, and she ought to thank him. It stirred her to do something other than doze. Her phone signal was poor, blown away, she felt, by the eternal wind. She headed across the rough field to the phone box in the empty car park by the shop.

'I've booked a flight. The end of next week. I've told Selina I'm up there on business. How's the house? I can't wait to see you.' Adam always sounded pleased to speak to her, his words lapping warmly around her. 'Are you feeling any better now?'

Her voice, not properly used for several days, was dusty; her tongue felt large and clumsy. She told him carefully that it was lovely, perfect, that she was having a great time, and she was looking forward to seeing him.

'What are you up to all day? Reading, are you? And walking? Have you made a start on that novel yet? You can show me what you've written when I come up.'

She paused. 'Yes, I could, couldn't I?' Then she lied and said, 'My money's about to run out. I'll call you soon,' and put the phone down.

She needed to buy food. The man who served in the shop greeted her as if he knew her. She bought apples and milk and a roundel of bere bread from the stack on the counter, and chose a postcard of the Brough, thinking she would send it to Adam.

Though it was June she lit the peat in the woodburner for the comfort of it. She sat in the armchair and picked up a pen. She couldn't send the postcard to Adam's house, and she didn't know what to write anyway. The thought of him made her feel jaded with the effort of being someone likeable. Tall and broad he would take up too much room in Zanzibar, his favourite black jumper with its pale stains stretched smooth over his belly as he lay on the two-seater settee, arms behind his balding head, feet lolling off the end. But then she remembered how, when they walked together, he put his arm round her shoulders and drew her in, how they chatted and shared, how they agreed and disagreed amicably.

But now he wanted her to be writing. The things she had thought of writing, when she was working and had never had time anyway, seemed facile and pointless. She plucked at two or three ideas and held them by the neck as they struggled to be free. She drew the curtains and put a blanket the colour of the beach pebbles over her knee and switched on the radio. She opened a bottle of red wine and drank it fast and had some brilliant and lucid ideas that she scrawled on the paper bag the bread had been wrapped in. Tomorrow she would make a start. She fell into bed.

The next morning there was rain in the wind from the north and the sky was as grey as the stones, as the sea. She was cold and ashamed of being hungover when she had been drinking alone. She took an unsatisfying shower that steamed up the bathroom and made the pine-clad walls drip. The towel she dried herself on was still wet from the day before.

91

She sat at the table in the living room with the bread and a jar of raspberry jam. She ate and ate and overate, pushing the food into her gullet. She made coffee and drank too much of it. She read the notes she had written last night and wondered where the brilliance lay. She plugged her laptop in and sat in front of it. She wrote a sentence, then another, and deleted both. The drizzle lay in a low mist over the grey houses and pain pincered her head. She wrote a postcard to Adam, 'Weather grey and wet. Perfect for creativity', and put his business address on it. Then she put on her wellingtons and her waterproof and shoved her camera in her pocket and, for the first time since she had arrived, walked onto the beach.

She would take some photographs, and they could feed her writing. It seemed a suitably creative thing to do. Her hair blew in her mouth and across her carefully framed shots of rock pools and the Brough. Rain ran into the lens. The light was poor. She put the camera away and headed unsteadily away from the settlement. The tide was pulling out and the bladderwrack and thick belts of kelp, beaded with periwinkles, were layered deep and slippery. They stank. The gulls stood on one leg or lifted themselves with ease into the eddying wind. She walked as far as the causeway then turned into the wind so her hair was swept back off her face. On the other side of Zanzibar squatted St Magnus's church and the smear of houses by the shop. All were walled round with slabs of dry-stacked stone. Zanzibar had a foolish picket fence that the wind blew straight through. It would be a task, she thought, to build walls like that, hefting the stone up the bank from the beach, but she had seen in the gardens next to the shop how the walls broke the wind and let the dark earth grow tomatoes and beans and carrots in the lee. She wondered if she would be at Birsay long enough to make a vegetable plot.

The wind was scraping her hangover away. She would go back and look at her photos and try again with the writing. She would write for an hour, she thought, just an hour, maybe start a diary; it couldn't be that hard.

The front door, which led straight into the living room, was ajar when she got back. She had not bothered to lock it when she went out. She hurried inside but it was easy to glance and see no one was in the house. She hung her coat over the bath to drip and went into the narrow kitchen to put the kettle on.

It surprised her, how big the bonxie was, its dirty brown head reaching as high as the hob. It took up most of the kitchen. And it regarded her sideways with its eye glittering before shitting fluidly on the floor.

Quickly she reached the sweeping brush from the corner by the door, and poked the bristles towards the bird. It opened its great hooked beak, took a couple of steps back and half unfolded its wings. They brushed the cupboards on each side. She could see this was not going to work. To goad the bird out of the kitchen she needed to get behind it and there was no space to do that. Surely it didn't really want to be in her kitchen. She decided to leave the kitchen door open, and opened the front door as well so that the bird could simply walk out by itself.

She climbed onto the bed and drew the curtain, leaving a little chink so she could watch. Her jeans were wet where the rain had dripped off her waterproof. She took them off and feeling cold she climbed under the covers. She would sit in bed and write, she decided, and reached for some paper and a biro, but the light was too poor for her to see properly. A tide of cold weariness laid her down, and she inadvertently slept.

She couldn't tell what time it was when she woke. She never bothered to charge her phone, and the only clock in the house was in the kitchen. She drank the bottle of water from last night that she found among the bedsheets. She was hungry too. Very hungry. She thought of the bread and jam she had left on the table. And then she remembered the bird.

She peered into the kitchen. There was a brown, greasy feather among the shit on the floor, and a foul smell of fish, but the bonxie wasn't in there. She boiled the kettle, ran a bowl of bleached water and cleaned the floor.

Because the front door had been open the rain had come in and made the house even colder. She thought she would light the woodburner again. She squatted down and opened the glassed door and began raking in the ashes. From this low position she noticed the hunks of bread pecked into crumbs, and the jam jar rolled under the table. Now she could see the bonxie hunkered down on the rug, its neck drawn into its shoulders, jam smearing its beak. It regarded her sideways with a slight yaw of its beak.

At least now she could get behind it. She took up the brush and stepped carefully, smoothly, round the armchair. The bird was already up, and instead of backing away from her had turned round to face her, rearing up and spreading its great wings, knocking papers stacked on the side table, the lamp, stretching forward so she could see its tongue in its beak and a brightness in its throat. It began jabbing at the brush head, and at her hands. She realised she was shouting at the bird, shrieking maybe, and the bird was cawing in reply. She swept at its wings, at its neck and head with the broom, but the bird reached past, lunged at her hand and drew blood. She yelped, dropped the brush and retreated. It followed a step or two, flapped and fluffed, preened a little, regurgitated on the rug, and settled down. She ran her hand under the tap and wrapped it in a tea towel. She sat on the worktop and drank coffee looking out into the dismal grey, watching the flashing codes of the lighthouse on the Brough.

At least she was in the kitchen so she could eat. Her headache was coming back. She put a potato in the microwave and ate crisps while it was cooking. Her hand throbbed, more bruised than bleeding, though she wondered what germs a bird might carry.

She would take the radio into bed, draw the curtain and slide the door across, and lie there and listen. She would leave the front door open all night and surely the bird would be gone by morning. It would be hungry again, and thirsty. She wondered if birds drank and if they did, what sea birds drank when there was only salt water. If she could have connected to the internet she could have googled it. It was early but the heavy darkness inside the bed pressed on her and she slept before the news came on at ten.

She woke at four with the news headlines. She needed a pee. Slowly, quietly, she swung her legs out of bed and moved towards the light switch. In the second before her eyes adjusted, she thought she saw the bird had its head buried deep under its wing, but in the same instant it was awake and had risen onto its webbed feet and spread its great wings and was hissing and advancing toward her. She ran into the bathroom and locked the door.

The bathroom was still wet. She sat on the closed lid of the toilet, and with her elbows on her knees she put her head in her hands. This is not good, she thought, I am so miserably alone. If I had anywhere to go, I would go. The bonxie must have been outside the door as she opened it, because it edged into the bathroom and extended its stout neck and stabbed at her with its beak, but she managed to twist past it and slam the door, shutting the flight feathers of one large wing in the jamb.

There was more shit on the living room floor, and shed down too, and a smell of half-digested fish, but at least she could reclaim the room for herself now. She chose not to think how she would get it out of the bathroom. She shut herself back in the bed.

In the morning she listened at the bathroom door, then knelt down and tried to peer through the crack above the threshold. She could see nothing though she could hear scratchings and the occasional coarse cry. She wondered how long it would survive without food.

This troubled her. All day long, when she had to drop down onto the beach to pee and take a crap, the bird was in her mind. She wanted a bath. She washed in the kitchen sink next to the plates and mugs on the draining board. Adam was coming, the house stank and she was too unsettled to pretend to write. She went through the photographs she had taken. They were blurred and colourless; she could not recall the significance of them. The bird had to be gone before Adam came. She would tempt it out.

She bought two tins of sardines. She would lay a trail of fish and lead the bonxie into the garden. Cautiously she opened the bathroom door, the lid on the tin of fish pulled back. The bonxie was on the edge of the bath, its dark eye level with hers. It shuffled sideways towards her. She held out a fish between her fingers, tempting the hungry bird, ready to drop the fish quickly. It watched her for a moment, then reached out and yanked the tin hard through her fingers, dropped it in the bath, bobbed into the bath itself and pecked the fish out. While it threw back its head to let them down its gullet she slammed the door. Drops of oil and blood dripped on the floor; the tin had sliced cleanly and deeply across all four fingers of her left hand. She wrapped her hand thickly in kitchen roll, pressed the flesh hard and raised it above her head. She was weary of the bird. She just wanted it out of Zanzibar. She allowed herself to cry.

The bleeding stopped. Her fingers were sticky and sore. She stuck plasters over the flaps of skin. She made up her mind. She would starve the bird out.

The weekend passed. She avoided thinking about the bonxie, just as she avoided the room it was shut in. Her kitchen became her bathroom, with shampoo and razor on the windowsill. The only mirror in Zanzibar was above the bathroom sink, so a couple of times she sat in the passenger seat of her car and looked in the mirror on the back of the sun visor, but most of the time she did not care about her appearance. The weather brightened, and although it was still breezy she sat in the garden with her back against the house and read. On Monday she even drove into Kirkwall and phoned her daughters and chatted to Adam. 'I'll be with you on Friday,' he said, 'I'll get a taxi from the airport and see you at tea time. I can't wait to be there.' She found herself smiling.

On Tuesday she listened at the door again, and heard nothing. Carefully, slowly she opened the door a crack, just enough to see the bonxie huddled in the bottom of the bath, its feathers ruffled up around it and its head drawn in. The room stank and the bath was spattered; dappled feathers lay on the floor. The bonxie barely turned its head; its eye was dull. Oh my god, she thought, I am killing this bird, this cannot be right.

Adam was coming. He would help her to get it out of Zanzibar. Meanwhile she put some fish and some water in dishes, and cautiously, cautiously, put them in the bath within the reach of the bird. The bonxie, still hunched low, spread its wings as best it could and lolled its head sideways, shamming dead. She drew back to watch. It took no interest in the food.

By the evening it seemed the bonxie had grown smaller. It took quick, shallow breaths that barely raised its chest. It did not shift when she came in. She poured some water past its beak, and held out a sardine by its tail, but the bird did not acknowledge them. It is dying, she thought, by morning it will be dead. She slept a guilty, restless sleep.

But in the morning the bonxie was still miserably alive, slumped from the effort of breathing, its eyes slitted. I will help you, she said quietly. Its feathers were warm and oily and deep; it took her a moment to find the solidity of its neck. She grasped it firmly; the bird was still beneath her fingers. She looked away, wrenching upwards and twisting. It took less strength than she had supposed. The bonxie flustered for a brief moment, then lay with its head hanging awkwardly. She stroked its back, its chest, the hollow feathers of its wings. She lifted it up and held it in her arms, its wings loose and spreading, its neck swaying, and carried it out of the house and tossed it down the bank onto the sand and pebbles.

When she had scrubbed and swilled the bathroom, she had a long bath. Leaving the window open she could hear the birds on the shore.

* * *

'How's the writing going?' Adam asked. They were standing side by side at the end of the garden, pressing in towards each other, needing to touch, looking over the shining sea towards the Brough.

'I don't think I want to write a book,' she said, 'I'm not sure I have it in me.'

'No? What will you do then?'

'Just get a job. Anything.' She turned to look at him. 'Do you mind?'

'Of course not. Why should I? You know, Ava,' he said, sighing heavily, 'I really do love you,' and he took her hand and led her down the slope onto the beach.

The bonxie's body had been ripped open, its body hollow, its greasy flesh scavenged, a few feathers straggling and lifting in the brisk breeze.

The sun glinted briefly off something within its ribcage. Ava watched as Adam knelt down and pulled out a twisted silver band, dulled by the crud of dried entrails. He scratched at it with his thumbnail and rinsed it in a shallow dip of water and rubbed it on his jacket. 'Isn't this beautiful?' he said, holding the ring up to the bright sky so she could see the loops and piercings around it. 'Do you reckon it would fit you?' and he slid it with care onto one of Ava's sore fingers. 'What do you think?'

Ava did not look at Adam, but watched for a moment as the last glimpse of the causeway was submerged in an eddy of sea. 'I think I want you to come and live with me in Birsay. I think you can run your business up here, and I think I'll be able to help you, and we can walk on the beach at midnight in summer and read books all winter, not in Zanzibar, but in a proper house that keeps the wind out and...' Ava turned to face Adam.

He was smiling. 'Let's do it,' he said.

JO HOLMWOOD

Porn Star Names

Thursday night. Shay gets a slab of cans in the Spar shop, which is all strip lighting and baldy tiles. The booze section is done out like a mock Spanish cellar. Except everything is plastic. At the counter, Shay digs into his pockets for a twenty. It's in there somewhere, scrunched up with an old Lotto ticket, a few coins, and some roaches – handmade from bits of cardboard that he ripped off his Rizzla packets.

'Cold out,' the girl at the till says. It's a rote offering, mechanically delivered; as mechanical as the scanning of the bar codes and the fingering of notes and coins.

'Brass monkey variety,' Shay says. The girl notices him then, smiles. He can't help but let his eyes drift down her neckline towards an impressive bosom, all covered over by her black uniform top. No hint whatsoever as to what lies underneath, but there's always the imagination.

Shay nudges the front door, which is open already and the key in the latch for all to see. Inside, the air is thick with the weed and the coal fire. Fitz and Martin are there already, poking at the fire and sucking on fags, their bottles and cans placed carefully around the room like skittles ready to be knocked down one by one. Their reedy laughter echoes around the kitchen-living room, which is decked out in the best décor from the seventies and hasn't seen so much as a new lick of paint since.

'What the fuck, O'Shea?' says Fitz, with a mock-indignant air and jabbing a finger in the direction of the Sacred Heart, which is balanced on a flower pot on Shay's dresser. It's got fairy lights draped around it – a rehash of last year's makeshift Christmas tree, which Susie helped him dismantle last week, even though it's tipping October.

'What?'

'Gone all Roman Catholic on us now?' Martin chips in, laughing.

'Found it in the cupboard under the stairs,' Shay says, taking control of his space; poking at the coal with an expert twist of the old poker, which nips at the skin if you hold it a certain way; organising his cans methodically, one at a time, into the fridge, which is empty but for a soft clove of garlic, the only trace of a Sunday roast he cooked up for the lads (and Susie) two weeks since.

'Why d'you get it out?' Fitz demands.

'Retro-chic iconography,' Shay says, sitting on a stool to roll himself a ciggie. 'Susie put it there for a laugh.'

'The fairy lights make him look happier,' Martin says.

'Yeah, he looks like he's tripping!' Fitz is doing a dance in the kitchen, his long legs restless; his fingers working at a bit of weed, breaking it down over a thin straggle of tobacco, which is limp and dry as a streak of lichen, laid out on a Rizzla on the kitchen counter. Shay's little Roberts radio is spinning out late-night eighties and nineties classics, but with the volume low. Morrissey is mourning like a looing cow from the reaches of the cold-tiled corner.

'Plus it reminds me that I did have morals once, back when they used to drag me to confession.'

'Morals! Nobody gives a shite about morals,' Martin says.

A clatter at the front door, followed by a spool of foolish laughter.

Spud and Donal burst into the living room, the fibres of their clothes glistening with the icy cold of the outside. They rush towards the fire.

'Donal didn't realise the door was open!' Spud says, still laughing, scrunching up his paper bag, from which he has already produced a noggin of whiskey. 'He fell flat on his face in the hall. His cans went everywhere. It was so funny! He was sprawled out like a lizard.'

The others are laughing, more from the double-act of Spud and Donal than whatever it is they're talking about. Donal has a put-upon demeanour, accepting of his eternal clumsiness, while Spud takes an air of pseudo-masculine superiority, jibing him and physically overshadowing him with his heavy bulk. Underneath it all, everyone knows that Spud is a pussycat.

'He's literally beating the door down!' Fitz says, smoke swirling around his head like steam from a witch's cauldron. 'He can't wait to worship at the new shrine.' He points at the Sacred Heart.

'What's that?' Spud says, taking a load off on the two-seater settee, throwing Martin halfway to the ceiling in the process.

'My new icon,' Shay says. 'A bleeding heart with a disco flavour.'

'Nice.'

'A bit of Zen for when I've got the DTs.

'You call that Zen?' Donal perches on an old crate that Shay has had under the kitchen table for an age; takes out a slim line cigar and lights it.

Such eccentricities are largely overlooked by the others, who know him too well. Even his voice is eccentric, slightly reedy and soft. His hair falls in limp strands over his ears in a long bob.

'Yeah, well...'

Shay takes the coal bucket and goes out the back door. He likes to keep busy when others are at his place. Like Fitz, he has to be moving; pacing and ordering. Especially when he's 'hosting', even in the most casual sense of the word.

'Hey,' Spud leans forward on the tiny wooden-frame settee, his fat forearms hanging over his knees. He pulls up the noggin to his lips and tips a little of the whiskey into his mouth. It barely looks like a wetting of the lips – everything in small measures for Spud, in spite of – or maybe because of – his size.

'I found out my porn star name today.'

'What?' says Fitz, still hopping around in the kitchen, never able to keep still. 'What you on about?'

'My porn star name. Haven't you heard of that before? You take the name of your first pet and your ma's maiden name and put them together.'

Everybody's eyes move skywards, while they work it out. Tears for Fears are making sounds in the corner. Donal makes an elaborate sucking gesture on his thin cigar.

'Rex Sameyovitch,' he says.

'Ah for fuck's sake,' Fitz cries. 'Trust you to have one that sounds more like a seventeenth Century Russian philosopher!'

'Can't help it. Me ma's Russian 'ain't she?'

'The less said about that the better,' Spud pipes up. 'What's yours Fitzgibbon?'

Fitz is smiling.

'Goldie McGee,' he says. The lads fall about laughing. Donal nearly falls off his perch and has to rebalance himself. The wobble makes them all laugh some more.

'Fuck me,' Martin says, from his comfortable post on the couch, pressed into Spud by the sheer force of gravity that Spud's weight causes. 'That's fucking spot on. That is such a porn star name if ever I heard one!'

'What's yours then, Martin?'

'Fluffy Malone.'

'Not bad, not bad,' Fitz calls from the kitchen. 'What's yours Spud?'

Spud grins, pleased with himself. 'Thumper Fox,' he says.

'Thumper, yeah that'd be right. What was that, a rabbit?' Donal sucks on a can. In this regard, at least, he is normal.

'Yeah. Lop-eared. Kept escaping. Spent days chasing the feckin' thing around the place. We nearly renamed it Houdini.'

'Houdini Fox. Not bad either,' says Martin.

'Jesus Spud, I can't see you with a rabbit.' Donal licks the beer from the top of his can, then darts a look at Spud.

Shay comes in the back door with a bucket of coal to heap on the fire. He catches the tail end of the conversation.

'What? Spud's shagging a rabbit?'

They all laugh.

'No, O'Shea, he had one when he was a kid,' Fitz says.

'Oh yeah?'

'Did you have any pets when you was a kid?' Fitz winks at the others.

'Yeah, a dog.' Shay is hefting the bucket into the corner by the fire, where wood and cardboard and papers and magazines are stacked. He picks up a few coal pieces that have spun loose with the tongs and balances them meaningfully on top of the existing carbon pyre.

'What was its name?' says Martin, picking up on the game.

Spud smiles, a huge fat foot tapping gently with expectation.

'Uh... Rasher,' Shay says.

A ripple of giggles.

'Don't ask. It had a kind of wavy pinkish-brown coat, with a sort of golden rind – the dead fur I suppose.'

More giggles.

'Hey, Shay,' Donal says, not able to resist cutting to the chase. 'What was your ma's maiden name?'

'I know what youse are getting at,' Shay says, finally stopping to take a few swigs from his can which is on the mantelpiece – a meanly decked faux-mahogany shelf, surrounded by crude square stone cladding that was all the rage some thirty years ago. 'My porn star name.'

'Can't believe he knows about that,' Martin mutters into Spud's shoulder.

'So, what is it then?' Fitz says.

'Rasher Crawley.'

A murmur of disgust.

'Uh, that doesn't sound very enticing,' says Donal. 'Sounds like a dodgy lice-ridden porn star with carpet rash!'

The others laugh. Donal stubs out his cigar and blows hoops from the remains of the last drag, his mouth opening and closing, *wow-ow-wow-ow*. The image reminds Spud of Fitz's porn name.

'So you had a goldfish, did you Fitz?' he says.

'Yeah,' says Fitz.

'Makes sense.'

'What d'you mean?' Fitz is slowing down now; the weed taking effect.

'Well, they go round and round and round, don't they? Never stop.'

'Yeah,' Shay chips in. 'And they have a memory of about a minute. That sounds about right.'

'I've a good memory,' Fitz says, defensive. 'I remembered me ma's maiden name, didn't I?'

The room is quiet for a split second. Each man is feeling the effect of his drink, his smoke.

Martin wriggles up from the fringes of Spud's craterous pull.

'Hey, speaking of porn stars, I found this thing on YouTube...' He pulls out his phone and begins tapping and scrolling. The others lean in with vague interest.

A tap on the pane at the back door.

They all jump.

'Only me,' says Susie, opening the door ajar and poking her head in. She sees the huddle, the guilty faces.

'What'ya all looking at?' she says.

Mumbles and murmurings as the lads pull apart again.

'Nothin',' says Shay.

Susie knows it's not nothing, but she stays quiet. She is wrapped in layers from head to toe – a woollen coat, two scarves, a hat, loose trousers, the cuffs pulled in by boots and thick socks.

'Jesus Sus, you look set for a moon expedition!' Calls Spud from across the room.

'Feckin' freezing out!' she says.

The lads nod. The female presence placates them. They don't mind it.

'Hey Sus...' Martin is pulling himself up from Spud's crater again, an inane grin on his face.

'Don't!' Says Spud. But Martin charges in.

'Did you have a pet when you was a kid?'

'Uh, you mean like a cat or a dog?'

'Any kind of pet,' says Fitz.

'Yeah.' Susie doesn't give them an inch.

'What was its name?' Martin calls, pushing for the joke; the laugh. Donal pulls out a new slim line cigar, runs his fingers along it, like he's stroking a caterpillar, puts it under his nose. The corners of his mouth curl. He is keeping still and quiet since, in Susie's company, he is even clumsier than usual.

'Is this the porn star name thing?' Susie says. They all deflate. The potential of the moment is lost. 'That doesn't work with me,' she says.

'What? Why not?' Fitz is half reclining on Shay's kitchen counter, a mud-caked boot hoisted onto the grimy Formica near the sink. He's always quick to lose the plot.

'Arthur Spallen. Nothing sexy about that.'

Shay watches Susie as she puts groceries in his cupboards. Nobody else has noticed this homemaking, their thoughts on drink and porn star names. The very word 'sexy' from Susie's mouth fills Shay with longing.

'Arthur Spallen?' Says Fitz in disbelief. And then in a mock formal tone: 'A worse porn star name cannot be conceivable.'

'I know. Like I said, it doesn't work.'

'You had a pet called Arthur?' This is Spud, reaching for a can over Martin's head, the settee creaking under his weight as he moves. He tosses it to Susie who catches it expertly.

'Yeah it was my neighbour's donkey. And when my neighbour died, we adopted it. They live to a good age you know. Forty or something.'

'Fuck, even in human terms, that's not bad,' says Donal, who regularly contemplates his own mortality.

'Even still. Who calls a donkey Arthur?' Spud upends his whiskey bottle in another short little jerk, squints just perceptibly with the flavour. Susie is holding the can in her hands, running her forefinger around the rim of its upper end. Shay watches as she calmly sets it down without opening it; busies herself again; picks up the conversation.

'Lovely creature, he was. Very gentle. I adored him.' Shay knows about Arthur the donkey. Susie has told him before, during one of their weed-fuelled heart-to-hearts. He has pictured her as a girl, tending to the animal in the field, feeding it nuts, stroking its face. Somehow the mythical donkey has contributed to Shay's overall appreciation of Susie, his adoration of her.

'Christ, it's warm,' she says, as the heat of the room, the bodies, begins to filter through.

She peels off layers. The boys pretend not to watch, but the scarves are unwound, the coat unbuttoned. Shay tries to be gentlemanly, taking these items from her and heaping them on a chair in the corner. He slides a glance at her belly. Definitely showing more now, although he wouldn't expect any of the others to be attuned to such things.

Except that Susie's breasts have definitely swollen, and that's the kind of thing less likely to go unnoticed.

Fitz has resurrected himself and gone into the back yard for some air. Donal's eyes are opening and closing, a mirror image of his mouth with the cigar smoke hoops. Martin is gazing inanely at a blank TV screen, and Spud is scanning a weekend magazine – one from the pile in Shay's corner that date back years.

'Here, look at yer wan!' He says. 'Look at the fucking plastic lips!'
Martin snaps back.
'She wrecked herself,' he concedes.
'Yeah, it's like an addiction, that plastic surgery shite.'
'Once you start, you just want to tweak and tweak and tweak.'

Susie raises a finger, beckons Shay to the dresser.
'Is it showing?' She asks, under her breath. Shay shakes his head.
'But you'll have to tell them eventually,' he says.
He knows the whole story. There's a sense of privilege to being Susie's confidant. He saw the whole thing as it unravelled. She was working in a bar over the summer in the local seaside town, turning heads with her thick long brunette plait and big brown eyes. Every day that she went down there, Shay felt the stabs of jealousy, knowing full well there would be chats and flings and dates, and no doubt a passionate encounter or two in some dark corner of the beach, or on the narrow bed of some run-down weatherboard hostel. Something about the sun and the sea seemed to turn the whole world horny.

Sure enough, a lanky streak of piss called Sam, from England, put in an appearance; a well-honed blond surfer, younger than Susie, with a confidence that could draw a girl, but that was fierce hard for another fellow to swallow.

She was smitten, he could see that.

And what could he say; *I don't like the prick? The faux-innocent charm; the smug, poised, self-congratulatory cockiness of him.*

It had been unusually hot, with the windows of the old Victorian houses seeming to crack under the bulging brilliance of the ample sky. The rocks on the beach seemed to steam and swell, with the seaweed draped over them in dry languid fringes, emanating fishy wafts that in any other context would be repellent. Families with babies and toddlers and dogs set up camp on the sand, which usually looked dirty and tired, but which in the unerring sunlight, was airbrushed to a refreshed golden vibrancy. And then there were the surfers; the sun-touched, sandal wearing, smiling cohorts, who strutted with their boards, the wetsuits pulled tight over muscular upper bodies. Their evening drinking sessions were full of laughter and soporific beer swilling, their body language was magically endearing with its somehow carnal flavour.

Shay had pictured it a thousand times; the moment when Sam moved in on Susie. A few well constructed compliments and the glances across the bar; perhaps a brushing of fingers as coins were exchanged for pints. He himself had seen the white hairs on Sam's forearms, against the brown skin, had smelt the salt in his bleached hair, had spotted the pale freckles across his forehead and neck. Hell, even Shay could see the appeal, in spite of his hatred.

But when the summer ended, so did the affair. And that was that. No surprise, Shay thought. But Susie was distraught. Her spirit seemed sunken, her eyes dull. Around that time she had told him about Arthur the donkey: Arthur's loyalty, Arthur's longevity. There was something so childlike in this recollection, so honest. Perhaps no man could match the creature's loyalty, although Shay would do anything to try.

'I wanted to ask you something,' Susie says.

Shay snaps back, looks at her with surprise. 'I wanted to ask if I could stay just for a little while. In the spare room.'

Martin and Spud are laughing. Martin has his phone out again, and Shay hears the word *vaginoplasty* spoken more than once. Donal has his head on the kitchen table, and Fitz keeps tripping the light in the yard as he moves about. It goes on and off with regularity, Fitz's movement tracked like a zoetrope sequence in the flashes of light.

'Here?' says Shay, dumbly.

'Yes.'

There is a moment of quiet. Shay looks at the Sacred Heart of Jesus, the thorns wrapped around the muscle, constricting it. But there is also a halo of light shining out.

'If it's not convenient...'

'Of course,' Shay says, cutting across her, desperate for the silence not to be misconstrued. 'Of course you can stay,' he says. 'As long as you like.'

Susie smiles, squeezes his hand. He knows it will never be more than this. The spare room, the groceries. But he doesn't care. And in six months' time, fuck knows what they'll do. He smiles back.

105

Susie jumps with fright. Fitz's face is at the window, his lips suctioned on to the glass, his eyes crossed.

'Come in,' she says. 'It's freezing out. You'll catch your death.'

'Brass monkey variety,' Shay says, half to himself.

'Hey Sus,' Spud calls. 'Have you heard of *labiaplasty*?'

'Can't say I have now. What is it?'

'Women getting their *loo-las* touched up,' says Martin, breathless with disbelief. Spud clips him one round the ear.

'Ow!'

Donal pulls his head off the table, like it's been fastened on with glue. Shay goes to the fridge for a new can. Susie has put butter, cheese, eggs and ham in there.

'Crazy what people do to themselves,' Martin observes. He has slid back into Spud's armpit.

'Crazy,' Spud says.

'Yeah. Crazy,' repeats Shay.

RIZWAN PIRACHA

Lateef's Room

'Watch this', Lateef says and he reaches under the goat and starts pulling and squeezing. I bend down so I can see the milk squirting into the little plastic bucket. It looks like he's pulling quite hard but the goat just stands there chewing, moving its mouth from side to side. He's made a lead out of rope and tied it to the mango tree but you can tell the goat's in no hurry to escape. It might be if it knew Eid's only two weeks away. Or if it was me yanking on those dangly things. It'd be bleating and struggling all over the place. Lateef though, I reckon he must've done this stuff all the time back in his village. I almost ask him if he did but I stop myself. They might not like it, people saying things like that.

He stops when there's maybe a glassful in there and then stands up and lifts the bucket to his mouth. He doesn't lower it till all the milk's gone. Some of it trickles down his chin and he wipes it with his sleeve. He looks down at me and says, 'Fresh goat's milk. Builds a man's strength.'

I'm sort of relieved he didn't offer me any. He puts the bucket down by the tree and says, 'The boss has guests tonight. I'm making chicken.'

He always calls Mr Hussain the boss. And I suppose he is Lateef's boss. It's just you never hear servants use the word like that, calling their master the boss.

'I'm off to Al Falah now to get some', he says. 'You coming?'

My friend Kashif's coming round in half an hour. I'm about to ask Lateef how long we'll be but then I just say, 'Okay'.

Mama won't let me ride in traffic so we've only got Lateef's bike. I sit on the crossbar with my legs on one side. It's always a bit wobbly when we set off but once we get going it's fine. Apart from the holes in the road and the drivers with their angry horns.

There's no clouds in the sky and it's a relief when we build up speed and the breeze hits us. 'That's more like it', I say. 'They said it'll cool down tomorrow though.'

'Who said?'

'The weather people. On TV.'

'That doesn't mean much. They're just guessing most of the time.'

107

I wonder if they had TV in his village. I'll ask Papa later, he might know.

'But they use... they've got all kinds of gadgets.'

'People don't die in floods because they forgot to watch the weather programme on TV, Salim.'

Now I'm feeling stupid, even though I know I'm right. I don't mind him teaching me about goats but this is different.

'I didn't say they can save people's lives or change the weather, I just-'

'Well, there you go. God makes the weather and what he makes he can change. Without warning. You'll understand these things when you're older.'

There's no way I'm going to convince him so I stop trying.

When we get to the chicken place there's a big sign saying how much it is but Lateef ignores it and asks the man. It must be like visiting a foreign country when he goes to the shops. Mr Hussain trusts him with the money though, so I guess he's learnt how to read numbers. Or he might know the notes and coins from their size. I don't want to ask him but I reckon I could find out some other way. Maybe just by watching him.

There's wooden cages stacked as high as my head, all full of chickens. They peck at the seed scattered on the floor of each cage. Sometimes they miss and peck each other's feet. The butcher grabs a chicken from one of the cages and Lateef nudges me. 'Now watch it dance'.

The butcher cuts off the chicken's head and throws the body into a little pit. The headless body jerks around, flapping its wings and kicking its legs. Blood spurts from its neck. He works fast and throws a second and then a third headless bird into the pit. They stagger about and bash into each other before slowing down like clockwork toys. Then they become still, twitching once in a while the way sleeping dogs do. The white feathers that've been flung up float back down. Kashif once showed me a snow globe his dad got him from Canada and it reminds me of that except for the red stains on the feathers.

When the butcher starts cutting up the meat his hands move so fast I keep thinking he's going to cut himself. I pull at Lateef's sleeve so I can whisper in his ear. 'Will he let us keep one of the feet? I want to show everyone at school.'

Lateef asks him and the butcher tosses one of the feet onto the pile of meat without replying or looking up.

When we're done Lateef looks at the change before putting it in his pocket but I can't tell if he counted it. He's in a more jokey mood on the way back, humming bits of songs and doing silly things to make me laugh. One of the roads goes downhill and he tells me to hold onto the handlebars when he lets go. I hold the bike steady while he flaps his arms and clucks like a chicken. Then I pretend to be a fighter pilot and make machine gun sounds at passing cars.

When we get home Kashif's waiting for me by the gate. He looks at his watch and makes a face. 'I told you I was coming at six.'

Kashif's dad went to Dubai last month and got him that watch. He has to make sure you see it wrapped around his pudgy little wrist every five minutes. Being punctual's a big deal all of a sudden. Lateef goes off to make dinner for the guests. Kashif doesn't bother saying hello to him. He waits till Lateef's inside.

'That the new neighbour you were talking about?'

'No, that's Lateef.'

'Lateef?'

'He works for… He's their servant.'

Kashif looks puzzled for a second and then rolls his eyes. 'Sometimes I don't know if you're sick in the head or just a bit simple. Is that his bike?'

I don't know why he's asking, he just saw us riding it.

'What about it?'

He looks around to see if anyone's watching and then kneels down by the bike. He starts fiddling about with one of the wheels and I hear air hissing out of the tyre.

'What're you doing that for?'

He ignores me. After he's done the second tyre he stands up and smiles. He takes a handkerchief out of his shirt pocket and starts wiping his hands like he's some kind of mechanic. 'Come on, let's go.'

He waves his hand in front of my face. 'Hello, anybody home? Come on Salim, the others'll be waiting at the pitch.'

He looks at his watch again. 'We've only got about two hours of light left.'

I should say something but it's not as if I can undo what he's done. I try not to think about it. I was looking forward to showing Kashif the chicken's foot. To be honest I still want to but I'm not going to.

* * *

It's Saturday and I'm going next door to see Adnan. The kids at school thought the chicken's foot was great but it's starting to smell a bit funny and I want to show it to Adnan before Mama makes me throw it away.

109

Maybe I could scare Saima, his little sister. They're having breakfast when I go round. Lateef's there but he doesn't look up. He's sitting on the floor in the corner eating a fried egg that Adnan hasn't finished. Sometimes their mum gives him leftovers if it's meat or eggs. I don't try to get his attention or anything. I never do when the grown-ups are there.

Adnan reckons the foot'll bring me good luck. 'Don't laugh Salim. Always keep it in your pocket. Specially when you're playing cricket.'

He's got me thinking now, but Saima clicks her tongue and shakes her head. 'How can something so horrible be lucky. That poor chicken, hopping around on one foot.'

They start arguing and I can't get a word in. I sneak a quick look at Lateef. He's finished eating and Mrs Hussain's giving him instructions about lunch. He's standing there with his hands behind his back and he keeps looking at the floor. He's doing more listening than talking and when he talks it's so quiet I can't make out what he's saying. I heard Papa tell someone Mr and Mrs Hussain had two kids and a boy who does the cooking. It sounded sort of funny when he said it, although he didn't act like he'd made a joke or anything. When he said boy instead of man.

I get home and I'm getting myself some water when Mama snatches the glass out of my hand. 'Don't drink from that glass... it's not clean.'

'It's okay, I washed it.'

'No no, it's only for Rasheeda.'

Rasheeda's the woman who comes to clean the house every morning but I've seen other people drinking from it so I don't know what Mama's on about.

'You let that builder drink from it.'

'It's for others... people who... people from outside. Outsiders.'

'What if... Can someone who lives next door be an outsider?'

Mama's got that frown she gets when she's about to put her hand on my forehead to check if I've got a fever. She shakes her head impatiently. 'So many questions! You'll understand these things when you're older.'

'Okay, whatever...'

I get another glass and Mama puts the old one on a shelf. She has to go on tiptoe to reach the shelf. I'm glad I'm not an outsider. Sitting in a corner eating my boss's kid's leftovers.

* * *

Adnan and Saima just got a puppy and I'm going round to take a look. Mama reckons they got it because they've become attached to the goat and Mrs Hussain thought they might get upset when it gets slaughtered on Eid.

Lateef's in the garden getting a pan of water for the goat. He smiles when he sees me.

'She gets thirsty in the heat. Drink up girl', he says, putting the pan down by the tree. He squats on the grass and watches the goat drink. I do the same, trying to get my body to move like his. Sort of like a wicket keeper but more relaxed. I lose my balance and nearly fall over. He looks like he's about to laugh but stops himself. 'I can get you a chair from inside if you want.'

It sounded like there was a bit of mockery in his voice. Or maybe there wasn't, I'm not sure now. I try to laugh but all I do is make a snorting sound through my nose. My face starts getting hot. I wish he'd just laughed, the way Kashif or Adnan would've. Just then Adnan comes out of the house with Saima and some of their friends. He's got the puppy and when he sees me he holds it up like it's a trophy. He puts it down on the grass and everyone stands around it in a circle. I get up to join them. Lateef ignores us for a while and then comes over.

We stroke the puppy's soft fur and let it lick our fingers. The girls all say how cute it looks and Saima picks it up and holds it like it's a baby. Adnan's patience runs out after about two and a half seconds. 'Come on Saima, dogs don't like that. Put it down.'

'It's a he, not a it.' She sticks her tongue out but puts the puppy down anyway, after whispering some soothing words in its ear.

'I reckon it's hungry,' Adnan says, 'that's why it keeps sniffing everything.'

He goes into the house and comes out carrying a plate with a bone on it. There's quite a lot of meat still on it. He puts it down under the puppy's nose and we watch it chew the bone and lick its lips.

Lateef doesn't join in or say anything, he just stands there looking at it. After a while he lifts his right foot and shakes it so his slipper falls off. He gently pokes the puppy with his big toe. Then he gives it a little push with the top of his foot. It rolls onto its back and flails about a bit till it's back on its feet. Saima looks upset but no one else seems bothered. I suppose Lateef must know how to handle animals, growing up where he did. He looks at it for a few more minutes and then walks off. We play with it for a while and then, one by one, the kids go off to find something else to do. When they're about to take the puppy back inside I bend down and stroke it where Lateef's foot touched it.

* * *

111

Lateef walks up to Kashif and stands in front of him, blocking his way.

'You like my bike, fatty?'

Kashif tries to look confused but you can tell he's scared. It's been more than a week and he must've thought he'd got away with it. Even I'm wondering how Lateef found out.

'Why did you take the air out of my tyres, fatty?'

He doesn't reply. I don't know if that's because he doesn't want to or because he's so scared he can't speak. Lateef smacks him in the face and his mouth falls open and his face goes red.

'Speak up fatty, why did you do it?'

Kashif's got this look on his face like he can't believe all this is actually happening. Like a part of him thinks he's going to wake up any minute, safe in his bed.

'If I catch you doing it again...'

Lateef walks off without saying what he'll do. I just stand there and watch the whole thing. It was wrong what Kashif did. I know I should've stopped him when he was doing it but still. There's no blood but Kashif takes out his handkerchief and wipes his mouth anyway. We're going to be late for practice but he doesn't look at his watch. We're silent most of the way and when we do talk it's about stuff that's got nothing to do with what just happened. Lateef didn't say anything to me when he was talking to Kashif. He didn't even look at me. The whole time, he didn't look at me once.

* * *

Lateef's room is a kind of shed attached to the side of the house. I knock and call his name but no one answers. There's no lock. I slowly push the door open. The room's quite small. There's a naked light bulb hanging from a wire in the middle of the ceiling. My head nearly touches the bulb so Lateef must have to walk around it. There's no fan and no windows. There's a creaky looking bed against the wall with a big dip in the middle. The only other furniture is a small table with a plastic plate and cup on it. And a page torn from a magazine. It's a black and white photo of some film actress but there's something's odd about it. I hold it up to the light coming from the doorway. It looks like someone's used a cigarette to burn a hole in the paper. Right where the actress's private parts would be. Out of the corner of my eye I see a shadow on the door and my heart jumps. There's no one there but suddenly it feels like someone could walk in any

112

second. The picture slips from my hand and I catch it as it falls but it gets crumpled. I put it back on the table and try to smooth out the creases. I'm breathing as if I've been running and the only sound I can hear is a humming in my head. I can't tell if anyone's outside. When I can't wait any more I pull the door open and run home without looking back.

DAVID SWANN

The War Against the Monsters

We'd just got settled when she called in: 'Only me, I'm not stopping!' and began the three-hour process of squeezing up the corridor, eating our light.

Finally, she arrived, breathless, at the threshold of our little room, gasping, 'Hallo, Madge. Hallo, Terrance.'

'Hallo, Aunty Brenda.'

In the gap between hearing her voice and seeing her face, there'd been enough time for Dad to bung a coat on and slip out the back. He hadn't been up to people since the factory gave him his cards. So when visitors came, he sat out in the shed, reading a Jack Higgins.

'Just two of you?' said Brenda, clutching the settee as if it were a promenade-rail.

'Hmmm,' said Mum, knitting.

I tried to block out Brenda's gasps. Tried to concentrate on my sci-fi film. The special-effects were good. Very realistic. Meanwhile, Brenda put her bulk into the settee. 'One of them nasties, ay, Terrance?'

'They're having a do with a monster, aren't they, Terry?' said Mum.

'With an *alien*, Mum.'

Brenda breathed deep, eyes on the warm hollow that Dad had left beside me on the settee. There were tell-tale flakes in the dip. Bits of dried-up paint.

'Alan out, then?'

'Mmmm.'

Something clattered in the back-yard.

'Only I could have sworn I heard summat as I came in, love...'

'Could you, Brenda?'

'I mean, he's not out there now, is he, your Alan, trying to get in?'

'I shouldn't think so,' muttered Mum.

'Only you hear such stories, don't you, pet?'

'You do, love.'

'About prowlers and perverts, and that.'

'Terry – go and check,' said Mum.

'I'm watching the film, Mum.'

She scowled from her knitting.

At the window, I lifted a blind, saw Dad skulking with his Jack Higgins in the shed. Or happen a Harry Patterson. Because Jack Higgins was two people, apparently.

'Nowt there,' I announced.

Brenda nodded. 'Only it's best to be certain, isn't it, pet?'

'It is,' said Mum.

Brenda shook her head at the telly, where an alien with 10 tails was inching along a ventilation-shaft. 'They'll be copying that. Won't they, Madge?'

Mum's needles kept up their mantra.

'As if there weren't enough bother. What with perverts everywhere, and this mess up the rezz. Eh, Madge?'

'Rezz, love?'

Aunty Brenda pushed her weight into the settee. 'Didn't you hear, pet? It's in the papers, even the free-sheet. About the lad that drowned.'

'Drowned?'

'Drowned to death up on them top-doings. And only 14. His parents must be beside themselves.'

Mum stopped knitting, and stared at the needles. 'There's always trouble for someone,' she said, very quiet. 'Who was it, love? Did they give a name?'

Brenda stared ahead, so saturated with bad news that she seemed barely able to listen. 'They're blaming the meeja,' she said. 'These daft films....'

I tried to concentrate on the alien's metal-teeth. Tried not to take Brenda on.

'I mean, they watch all sorts, don't they, Madge?'

'They do, Brenda.'

'Like that one last night. Did you see it, love?'

Mum was knitting again, counting under her breath. The needles clicked. *Knit-one, purl-one. Knit-one, purl-one...* 'Last night, Brenda?' she asked, eventually.

'The very violent one. Where they cut off the fella's ear. The 18. I nearly had to turn it off.'

'I must have missed that one, love.'

'I only half-watched it. Like this – through my eyelashes.'

'Should have shut them completely, Brenda.'

115

Brenda snapped her fingers. They didn't snap – they made a dull clack. '*Reservoir Dogs*,' she said.

'Oh, aye...'

Aunty Brenda sighed. 'It'll have encouraged him, a young lad like that. Don't you think, Madge? Watching films about reservoirs? I mean, why else would someone go swimming? Up there? In this weather?'

Mum shook her head.

'He'll have gone down white and come up blue. Eh, Madge?'

'He will that, Brenda.'

'Because it's raw up there on them top-doings, isn't it?'

'It is. Raw, lass.'

'Not to mention the mud. It's deceptive muddy in that rezz, Madge. Same as all soft-spots. Like the lad who went off the bridge in Bristol. What's it called? That big bridge? Down South?'

'The Clifton Suspension Bridge,' I said quickly, before she clacked her fingers again.

'Aye, Terrance. The Clifton. Any-road, you'll know the story, won't you. About the suicide? The lad who jumped, Madge? Who hit the bottom and lived?'

'Good for him, pet.'

'That's just it, though, love. He went up to his neck in mud...'

'Like I said. Good for him.'

Brenda bunched her fingers. 'Not *that* sort of mud, Madge. Clinging mud. Mud you can't get out of, no matter *how* you struggle. Hours he were stuck, that suicide. Up to his neck in clinging mud. And then he came to – and do you know what he saw?'

'What, love?'

'A wave, rushing towards him. He saw the tide coming in, Madge. The Severn Bore.'

Mum stopped knitting. The only sound was Aunty Brenda's breath, a fist-noise from the film, the thing with metal-teeth hissing...

'They reckon his mouth were still open. From screaming. They're dangerous places, bridges,' said Brenda. 'So what I want to know is why they don't put nets under them. Eh, Madge? Like this do up the rezz... there ought to be nets there too, eh?'

Mum's needles gathered pace.

'Mind you,' said Brenda: 'they performed miracles, them ambulance-men. They got their vehicle over the tops, love. To the edge of the rezz. Which proves they know a thing or two . Eh, love?'

'Yes, Brenda.'

'Not like that mess last week. Did you read about it, Madge? Them ambulances answering hoaxes? And they crashed into each other? Imagine that, love. Horrendous, it said in the papers.'

Mum stared at her knitting as if it was the accident scene.

'The thing I can't stop thinking, Madge... who went to help *them*? I mean, that'd need another ambulance. A third ambulance. And what if *it* was on a hoax, too? The third ambulance? See, if the ambulances were all out on hoaxes, then...'

'Will you be wanting a brew, Brenda?'

Aunty Brenda faltered, smiled. 'Well, that'd be grand, love.'

'Terry!' said Mum.

I rolled my eyes. But I was glad to get away, even if it meant missing the film. From the kitchen, I heard Brenda settling into my place on the couch. Heard her flick away the paint left by Dad. As she settled, her coat crackled like a Geiger counter.

I let the kettle whistle for ages. It blocked out the story Brenda was telling Mum:

'... and then they attacked the ambulance-men. And they don't get special treatment, the ambulance-men, do they? They're left lying on trolleys too, aren't they?'

I brought in the tea and listened as Brenda slurped. Listened to Mum's knitting. Listened to more of Brenda's stories. Factory-workers who fell into vats of acid. Builders swiped by wrecking-balls. Quarrymen flattened by trucks. Casual workers sucked into industrial vacuum-cleaners.

Worse. Acts of God. The angler carried off by a freak-wave on the Leeds-Liverpool Canal. The little girl who didn't know, until too late, that she was allergic to terrapins. The tourist who fell off a ferry into the Bay of Biscay and lived, but got swallowed by a whale. A dinner-lady, scalded to death in her own home by steam-puddings. Two teenagers fond of flattening coins on train-lines, who survived their hobby, but got hit by a helicopter crashing into the railway embankment.

'Because you never know, do you, Madge?'

'You don't, Brenda.'

'Take them knitting needles of yours, for insta...'

Mum stood up. 'I'll just spend a penny, love,' she said. And rushed upstairs.

With Mum gone, Brenda fell silent while the television played between us – the alien lashing its tails at the astronauts, spitting with rage when they lasered it... lots of great stuff that I could barely hear for Brenda's Geiger Coat.

Upstairs, there came the sound of quiet tinklings from the loo. Mum's bladder problem. Which I knew for a fact to be water trickling from a jug into the toilet. Together, Aunty Brenda and I listened to the symptoms of my mother's made-up illness.

'Cystitis again, I shouldn't wonder,' Aunty Brenda tutted. 'It burns worse than fire. In the worst cases, it can ruin a woman's life. Contort her into... *shapes*. On account of the agony, lad. In your privates...'

After she'd finally come downstairs, Mum's place in the toilet was taken by Brenda, which allowed Mum to lay out her plan: she'd be off to bed early with her made-up illness, and I'd walk Brenda home. 'You're right – it isn't fair,' she said, when I protested. 'Because *life* isn't fair. It gives illnesses to some, and morbid natures to others...'

'But Dad never walks Brenda home.'

'Because of his nerves. Because he runs off when he hears people coming.'

'That time I ran off, you called me a little monster.'

'Aye. And your Dad's worse. Skulking in the yard! No wonder I'm ill!'

'But you used a jug!'

'And I'll use one on *you* if you don't stop moithering. You know Brenda gets nervous in the dark. She's all on her own, lad...'

'It isn't fair, Mum. Her own kids should be walking her home.'

'Well, they don't, do they. They're grown-up now. They hardly bother.'

'I'm not surprised,' I said.

Mum pointed the needles at me. 'Shame on you. Saying such things.'

'Well,' I said.

Neither of us spoke after that. We sat there, scowling. I tried to watch the film, but Brenda was moving about above us, and it put me off.

'What I don't get,' I said, eventually, 'is why she always comes when films are on, Mum? And talks all the way through about her insides. And the third ambulance. What's this third ambulance, Mum?'

Mum sighed, ran a hand through her hair. As she was about to speak, Brenda's coat crackled in the doorway.

'Worms,' said Aunty Brenda as she re-entered the room, re-adjusting herself. 'Probably with the sherbert I eat, love...'

By that point, I'd done as Mum urged, spreading myself across the couch, so there was no place for Brenda to sit.

'When the pain gets this sharp,' said Mum, putting down the needles and rubbing her stomach, 'the only cure's sleep...'

Brenda nodded slowly, watching Mum wince.

'Terry'll walk you home. Ay, Terry?'

I shook my head. 'If that's what Aunty Brenda wants, Mum,' I said.

Brenda folded her arms. 'Eee, he's a grand lad,' she said. 'I were only saying to your boss at the shop yesterday, love – he's turning into a right grand lad, is Madge's lad.'

Mum watched me from the corner of her eye. 'Did you hear?' she said. 'About how grand you're turning out to be?'

That shifted me, the embarrassment. I grabbed my coat, and led Brenda down the passage. She seemed to touch both sides of the corridor at once, the swishing she did.

'Don't come out, pet,' she called over her shoulder. 'A rotten night like this, you'll get a chill on your kidneys.'

Mum risked it, though. She stood on the step, waving as though Brenda was heading out to sea. Which, the size of her, maybe she was.

'Go in, go in,' said Brenda.

'Bye, love,' said Mum, arms folded to protect her kidneys. 'See you soon.'

'*In*,' Brenda shooed.

Slowly, Brenda pulled out into the major shipping-lanes, with me whizzing along in front like a tug. To make it worse, the drizzle had decided to stop messing about now. There was a wet fur all around us, like the first strands of a web. It would be tonking it down soon, and I'd have to trudge home through it.

Brenda walked so slowly, I knew I'd miss the end of the film. Plus, she kept mistaking sandbags for dead Labradors or split bin-bags for cats with their puddings hanging out. Steadily, things got more gruesome... until, passing the alley on her street where a broken streetlight was always buzzing and blinking, she pointed into the flickering orange glow, and said: 'Look. What's that, lad? That thing hanging off the wall? Is it a...'

'It's a ladder, Aunty Brenda. It's Bob Fletcher's ladder.'

She took off her glasses and wiped them. It didn't do much good. The lenses were wet as soon as she restored them to her face. But it was the first time I'd seen her eyes in real life. Without the glasses, I mean. And I noticed how small they were, the eyes of a mole, all squinty and weak.

'I've told that Bob Fletcher,' she said. 'I've warned him. Someone could walk under that ladder. Worse, lad. Walk *into* it. And what if Bob's up it when the legs skid out? Imagine that.'

'Nearly there, Aunty Brenda,' I put in. 'Just a few more houses.'

Neither of us spoke as she fitted the key to the latch of her door. It had finally all been said, I think – every possible disaster, all the tragedies anyone could ever imagine – and now there was just a long wet night stretching out in front of her.

Short of breath now, she ushered me in up the lobby, and waited for me to switch on the light. Her house stank of muscle relaxants. I nearly fell over, the waft was that bad. It smelled like a rugby changing-room.

It was very harsh, the light. It virtually burned out my retinas. Under its glare, Brenda looked over-exposed, all bleached-out and old. She was standing in the vestibule, waiting.

And I knew what that meant.

'If you wouldn't mind, Terrance,' she said. 'Only...'

It embarrassed her to ask, so I spared her that. I trooped upstairs and did my usual check for intruders. I looked under the bed and stared into the bath. Why the hell a murderer would want to hide in the bath, I'd no idea. But I did what she wanted. I didn't bother with the airing-cupboard, though. It freaked me out, that cupboard. There was no way I was looking in there.

Then it was time for that other chamber of horrors, Brenda's bedroom. This room faced out onto the street, and contained no sign anyone had ever slept there. It wasn't only freezing cold, but seemed somehow derelict, as if it had lost its purpose. The eiderdown was pulled down perfectly straight over the bed, and the one piece of furniture was a stiff, straw-bottomed chair. The weirdest thing about the chair, it faced the wall. Apart from that, there was nothing at all to look at, so I shuffled about, pretending I was conducting a thorough search when, really, I was just staring out of the window, watching it rain.

Downstairs, Brenda was busying herself, clacking together plates and cutlery. It was the most ominous sound I knew, an omen of some undrinkable beverage. For reasons I never understood, Brenda had got it into her head that I loved old-fashioned shit that she'd eaten and drunk when she was young, in the Boer War or whenever.

I lingered at the window, trying not to look at Bob Fletcher's ladder. It was hard to admit, but I shared Brenda's unease about that ladder, the way it stood there. I'd never liked that alley, and always put a spurt on whenever I passed. If I'd lived opposite that alley, I'd have turned my chair to face the wall too.

More clinking noises downstairs. I hated to think what she was preparing. Hot sarsaparilla juice and a plate of pig-nuts, most likely. Stuff she'd dug up off some wasteland. *It'll keep you regular, will that, lad. They taste a bit like celery, them pig-nuts, eh? Like a sharp version of celery.*

I went back across the landing to the bathroom and did a bit of trickling with Brenda's jug. I couldn't face going down yet, even though it was cold as the moors in her bathroom, and the smell of moss was almost over-powering. Plus, I could hear the airing-cupboard while I stooped over the toilet with the jug. The gurgling noises coming from inside, you'd have thought Brenda's house was digesting a big meal.

But, finally, there was no way to postpone it. I went downstairs.

It was just as I'd feared. There was a cup of what looked like tar waiting for me on a table between her two armchairs. And a few twists of what Brenda called 'Spanish' lying coiled up like dog-turds on a plate. The idea with the 'Spanish': you put it in your mouth and chewed it for about a year. It cleaned the gaps between your teeth, apparently. And did miracles for your innards. Napoleon had eaten it, she'd told me. On account of his gut-rot.

The hot sarsaparilla-juice brimmed between us. There seemed to be about a bucket of the stuff. Beside it, Aunty Brenda's pint of milky tea looked thimble-sized. It was hard to imagine ever drinking that much liquid. I couldn't manage my 'Spanish', either. Instead, I put it in my pocket and worked my jaw as if I were eating raffia-work. Which is what it tasted like, anyway.

'Is it good?' said Brenda, banking up the fire, bringing warmth at last to her mausoleum.

'Delicious,' I said, chewing like a dog.

'It'll keep you regular too, will that,' said Brenda, warming her hands. 'Your Uncle Alf swore by it when he was living. The same time every morning, he went. Like a Swiss clock.'

I nodded, nervous to hear Alf's name, particularly in connection with his bowels. There'd be a tear in the corner of her eye now, and it wouldn't fall, just lodge there like a silver cake-bead.

'You favour Alf a bit, now I think about it,' she said, slowly settling into the chair. 'Around the eyes, mainly. He was shy too. *Backward in coming forward*, I called him...'

I shuffled in the chair. It was nice to feel the fire, but if it had come to a choice between either sitting there nice and warm, or being trapped with an alien inside a rocket, I'd have gone for the alien.

She pointed over to the sideboard, at the only photograph in the house. It stood next to a pot-hedgehog that bristled with lollies. I'd never liked that hedgehog, with all its cracks and filaments. It had been white once, but Brenda's cigarettes had turned it mustard. As for the photo, it was even less appealing. Aunty Brenda was a neighbour, not a relative – and Alf certainly wasn't my uncle. In fact, he'd died before I was born – and the closest I'd ever got was that photo. The best I could tell, he'd been a hunched-looking bloke, who favoured corners, out of the wind. In the picture, he was in the queue for a cinema, staring off at something only he could see, his body angled away from the camera. THE TINGLER, it said on the poster. That's the film he was queuing for. Not one of Alf's favourites, if his frown was any guide. He'd been an awkward plank of a man, and it hurt to hear I was supposed to look like him, especially around the eyes. Because he had the eyes of a mass-killer.

'Aye,' she said, following my gaze – 'you can see it, can't you? The likeness? He was a lad for the films too. Not your nasties, of course – spy films, they were Alf's thing. Very confusing, most of them. I was always poking him: *Who's that supposed to be, Alf? Why's he following her?* But he'd only shush me and point at the screen. *Watch*, he'd say. *Listen*. I wouldn't have minded, but half the time, I could barely see anything. They were usually slithering around inside these tunnels. Which I blame for my macular degeneration. I mean, your eyes couldn't adjust. *Next time can we happen watch something outdoors?* I'd say. And he'd nod, that way he had. *Aye*, he'd say, *next time, love.*'

She lifted the glasses and rubbed her eyes. I got sad when she did that. I noticed her eyes again, how small they were. It made me feel tight to want to be in a rocket with an alien. I saw how mean-spirited I was, what a rotten neighbour.

'Yes, tunnels,' I agreed, chewing harder. 'Only, I reckon Mum will happen be wondering where I am by now, Aunty Brenda...'

'Aye,' said Brenda. 'She's a worrier, your Mum, ay? I've warned her: *It'll knock years off your life, all that fretting, Madge*. But you know the way some people are, Terrance. They're born like that, eh?'

I'd no idea how to answer that. I just sat there, thinking about the film. It would be coming to the climax now. There'd be brilliant explosions, probably. A blast that rocked the craft, all the oxygen flowing out...

'Well, I'll not keep you,' she said, at length. 'A young 'un like you, I'm sure you've plenty to be doing, eh? We'll just drink these, and then you can be off, lad.'

She sat on, staring at the photo. 'But the flea-pits where they showed them,' she said, with a long, weary sigh. 'Honestly. My skin used to *crawl*. They weren't even fumigated, some of them. That dump in the photo – The Gaumont. Hell's teeth, it was wick. You saw them in the projector-ray: lice and what-not. Fleas. I remember this one the size of a house that came over. I ducked, of course. But your Uncle Alf only sat there, sucking his boiled sweet. *Just a shadow, love*. That's what he said. Aye, and there even was a dog in the cinema that day. A stray-dog, off the street! I remember it as if it were yesterday, lad. Except clearer. Because I barely remember what I did yesterday...'

I concentrated on eating the pretend 'Spanish'. It was a good work-out for my jaw, at least. Not that anybody ever wanted a fit jaw...

'Listen at me, though,' said Brenda. 'Chewing your ear off. It'll be the last thing you want to hear about, eh? The lice in old cinemas?'

'Yes,' I said.

She laughed, seemingly from surprise. Then the laugh slowly disappeared into the cold places in her house, and another sigh rose in its place. This was a different sigh, though – more sad than weary.

'What *did* I do yesterday?' she said.

While she was trying to remember, I got up and made my excuses. It was wet, getting wetter. I didn't want to develop pneumonia, etc. If you put it in illness-talk, Aunty Brenda understood that. Before I scarpered, she did what she always did: called me her Angel Gabriel and gave me a treat from the hedgehog. It was a lolly that tasted of gear-sticks and I'd throw it, as usual, into Bob Fletcher's back-alley when I was rushing past.

I legged it off through the rain, trying to erase the kiss she'd planted on my cheek. It was stickier than ketchup and more or less the same colour, but I got most of it off, and then the kiss was on my hands, and I gave it up for a bad job.

When I passed the broken street-light, I stopped to study Bob Fletcher's ladder, hoping it wouldn't creep me out. The lamp-post trembled like a living thing. Under its flickery light, the smashed drainpipes tippled their water more loudly. The alley was as dark as a mouth. I stared into it. 'You're not scaring me,' I said to the alley. 'You're not even real.'

Then that was me: I threw away the lolly and dashed off like a whippet. I was drenched by the time I got home, but it was good to hear Mum's needles while I was taking off my coat. *Knit-one, purl-one...* There was something safe in that, the regularity.

I'd missed the end of the film, of course. And Mum wasn't exactly a fount of information. 'Dry your hair, lad.' That's all she said when I asked what had happened.

'Where's Dad?' I said, mopping the rain with a towel. 'Still in the shed?'

'How should I know?'

'But Brenda went yonks back. Didn't he come in?'

Mum kept knitting, pretended she hadn't heard. 'You took your time,' she said.

'Brenda gave me some 'Spanish',' I said, as if that explained anything.

'Did she talk your ear off?'

'A bit.'

'But you got her home?'

I nodded. 'Answer the question, though, Mum. Did they get it?'

'Get what, love?'

'In the *film*.'

'The monster, you mean?'

'The alien. Did they get the ALIEN, Mum?'

'A bloke in a suit, more like. Never seen anything so daft in my life.'

'How about Brenda's lollypop-hedgehog? That's dafter.'

Mum shook her head. 'I've warned you about that tongue,' she said. 'If your Dad ever comes in, he'll square you up, Terrance.'

I rolled my eyes. Like Dad would actually do that. Look up long enough from his Jack Higgins. 'Mum,' I said. '*Please*. Did they get the alien?'

She'd been knitting viciously, grinding her teeth. But now she stopped suddenly and sighed. 'Well,' she said. 'What do you reckon, Terrance? What *always* happens?'

'How would I know? I was looking under Brenda's bed, remember. Listening to sagas about lice.'

Mum blinked. 'O God. She didn't get onto *parasites*?'

'As if you care.'

'Look...'

'It's true. If you cared, you'd have walked her home, wouldn't you! Instead of inventing another illness!'

'Inventing? What do you know about women's complaints, Terry? You're 12-years-old.'

'Exactly. I'm 12-years-old, Mum – and a world-expert on tapeworms. Because I spend half my life with Brenda. If I have to listen about tapeworms again, I'll kill myself.'

Mum sighed in disgust. 'Don't be so dramatic, lad.'

'I mean it. I'll hang myself off Bob Fletcher's ladder.'

She stared at me, very hard and cold. 'That's sinful talk. Hear me?

124

You're not to say such things, or I'll put you over my knee and tan you. You're not too big, Terry. And not too old. And that sinful talk proves it.'

She let that settle, the way she always did. I knew I'd gone too far, of course. Knew it was to do with Uncle Alf. Nobody mentioned it, but I was pretty sure he'd killed himself. Brenda's family was a train-wreck, everyone said so. Alf dead. Their grown-up kids like strangers. No wonder she shut herself indoors with the local 'papers. The world outside was outer-space, an airless vacuum. It'd pour through the air-vents and kill you.

'Look,' I said. 'Mum. Can't you just say what happened?'

Mum shook her head. 'They killed it, what do you think?'

'How?'

'I don't know. With a pipe, or something. A bit that had fallen off.'

'And then what?'

'It died.'

'Just like that?'

'Well, they spun it out. All the usual rubbish,' she said. 'Apart from the last 15 seconds. The last 15 seconds were good.'

'Brilliant,' I said. 'Fifteen decent seconds.'

'See, the alien had these... death-throes. And it screamed so loud when they stabbed it, that everybody took cover.'

'The heroes, you mean?'

'Well, the people who were in it. Bruce Willis, and that woman in the bra.'

'Bruce Willis wasn't even in it,' I said.

'Whoever he reckoned to be. Anyway, he saved her, of course – put an oven-glove over her ears to block out the death-throes. Which is far-fetched, if you ask me. A bloke saving a woman.'

'Are you sure it was an oven-glove?'

'That sort of thing,' said Mum. 'Anyway, it didn't work. Not really. Because the monster's death-throes went out into space...'

'Except sound can't actually travel through space.'

Mum growled. 'Are you listening? Or being a cleverhead?'

'Listening,' I said.

'Good. Because we're on the last bit now. See, the scream travelled down to a planet, into a swamp. And you'll never guess, but there was another monster sloshing about down there, a bit like the first monster, except female. The monster's mother, probably. And it pricked its ears when it heard the death-throes.'

125

'Can you stop saying death-throes?'

'Not particularly,' said Mum. 'Because I don't know what else to call them. And anyway, I've finished now. The monster's mother heard the death-throes. And then it turned towards the camera, and let out a roar. And that was it, lad. The end, thank god.'

'Except for the sequel, probably.'

'Well, if there's a sequel, I hope I don't have to sit through it. Honestly. Blokes saving planets. They can't even save money to buy milk.'

Right on cue, Dad did a bit more clattering in the shed, probably dropping his Jack Higgins. They made the covers too shiny, he said. They were that shiny, you couldn't get a grip.

If he got another job, he'd be better then. He'd clear a few phantoms from the void. That's what the doctor had said. I'd patched it together when I listened through the floorboards. It felt good, that phrase. *Clearing phantoms from the void.* It made a taste in my mouth.

Phantoms, though. Phantoms and monsters. Why had they come here? What were they looking for? If they were so terrifying, how come they spent all their time hiding? And the places they chose! Airing cupboards, back-alleys...

Silly idiots, lurching about and groaning.

Except maybe the monsters were frightened too. Maybe they had their own monsters. I crumbled a few flakes of paint left by Dad, and imagined that: a massive queue of monsters, stretching back through the streets.

There'd be an end, though. All queues have an end. At the back, there'd be one final monster, all alone, with nothing after it. And one day, when I was older, I'd take Dad with me to ask that monster its secret, to find out how it had managed that.

To be a monster with no monsters.

JIM WAITE

Brylcreem Boy

Edinburgh 1960

It looked like yellow candyfloss exploding from the back of her head. I gave Charlie a nudge. 'How about that one? The one with the hair? Green dress?'

He looked at me with his usual knowing grin. 'No chance,' he said. 'That's big Donna. Not in your league. Used to go with Ricky Moran.'

Ricky Moran, the drummer up there in the band. Square face, square fists holding his sticks. He liked banging things, that's why he took up the drums.

'She chucked him last week,' said Charlie.

That decided me. 'Not in my league?' I said, patting my carefully sculpted hairstyle into place and wiping my hands on my backside to get the grease off. 'We'll see about that.' I puffed out my chest, pulled back my shoulders and stretched my spine to its full length. It hurt a bit, but I tried not to wince. I'd made up my mind: Donna was tonight's target.

We'd been there over an hour, painstakingly toffed up in brylcreem and uncomfortably tight trousers, standing by the door eyeing the talent. Dances were simple affairs all those years ago; just lights on in the college hall and a glitterball dangling from the ceiling. There was an old-fashioned band, with a trumpet and a saxophone; not a guitar in sight. You could hear what people were saying. You even had to talk while you were dancing.

It was easy, of course, for Charlie and me. A quick check of our hair in the cloakroom mirror, then we'd ask a couple of girls to dance. They usually jumped at it, because there were far more of them, and let's face it, we were pretty impressive. If we didn't really fancy them, because they chewed gum, or laughed through their noses, or had missed their mouths with the lipstick, we'd put on a fake accent and invent a story about ourselves, just for a laugh. It was a bit of a game.

Later on, though, you'd want a girl to let you see her home, and then the main thing was to choose one who'd impress your friends, give you something to brag about in the college on Monday. Donna with the candyfloss hair was just that.

I put the technique into action. So relaxed I was practically asleep, I sauntered over. Her friends tactfully turned away in mid-sentence. Looking through half-closed lids, I flicked my right eyebrow at the dance floor, questioning. She shrugged with her mouth, shifted the chewing gum into her left cheek and moved forward, hands raised to mine. There was no need to speak. As we began, I threw an exaggerated wink to Charlie and the others, all enthusiastically thumbs-upping from their corner.

Donna was much taller than I had thought, probably because of her shoes. It wasn't really necessary to dance, though, we just did a sort of one-two-one-two shuffle along with the music. The challenge was to avoid standing on her feet, which would ruin my chances. She seemed more interested in chewing her gum and looking over my shoulder at Ricky Moran than in me. I don't think our eyes met once, although we kept jogging on together. Between dances, we just stood there, not speaking, waiting till the band started again.

We chugged around like this for a bit. I was quietly singing in my best American, asking Donna if she was Lonesome Tonight, when I noticed that the lashes on her left eye were peeling off at one end, wriggling like a hairy caterpillar. I didn't like to say anything, it would have ruined the romantic mood.

During the next dance, however, as we skated down the slipperined floor in a clumsy quickstep, the thing leapt in the air and vanished under our feet. Maybe it thought her green dress was a giant cabbage. I pretended not to see, although Donna did look a bit unusual with one eye sprouting a lush canopy and the other almost bare. We shuffled on.

The last dance was always crucial; it decided the success or failure of the evening. The lights were turned off. Click, darkness. No subtlety in those days. Only the band, groaning sentimentally, still had some light. Donna pulled me towards her. Her chin jabbed my forehead. A stab of perfume pierced my nose and I sneezed down the front of her dress. She didn't seem to notice. Unsteadily, we stumbled round the floor.

She was strong, that girl. I didn't have much control. I had to teeter about on tiptoe. Donna had my face clamped against her neck, so I couldn't see where we were going, and some other girl's heel had pierced my ankle. I gritted my teeth and carried on, not wanting to spoil the blissful moment. Most of the lads around the hall would be sick with jealousy.

The dance ended, the lights flicked back on. The band, anxious to get home, struck up a few brisk bars of the national anthem. We all stood sheepishly. 'God-save-our-gracious-queen-long-live-our-noble-queen-

God-save-the-queen.' A crash of cymbals and that was it. The musicians picked up their instruments and headed for the door.

I narrowed my eyes and squinted at Donna, who was still gazing without interest over my shoulder. 'See ya home?' I drawled. There was a pause. I could see her thinking.

She shrugged. That meant yes, I knew the language.

I accepted the congratulations of Charlie and the others while Donna was finding her coat. A quick check in a mirror was enough.

'Perfect,' I thought. My reputation was assured. There was no sign of Ricky Moran, I was happy to see. It wouldn't really matter what happened later, as nobody would know about it except Donna and me. However, I thought I might as well make the most of things.

We walked down to get the tram to her part of town. Both eyelashes seemed to have escaped now, I noticed. Just as well. She was more balanced that way.

I'd have liked to hold her hand as we walked. The problem was it was too high and I'd have looked like a child toddling along with its mum. So I just hummed some dance tunes and did a bit of waltzing and jigging about. There wasn't much point in talking as Donna never answered, just tottered along on those heels, trying to hold her hair together in the freezing Edinburgh fog.

We reached the tram stop, a single yellow eye lurched towards us, and number one-six-seven clanked into view. I saw the conductor giving Donna a good look over as we climbed the stairs, and that made me feel better.

Sitting upstairs on the tram, we didn't have much to talk about. Donna produced a crumpled bag of chocolate caramels and offered me one. That was a good sign. I rewarded her with my special Presley smile, the twisted one with my lip curled at one side.

Working through the bag filled the time nicely. You couldn't speak with your mouth clogged full of sticky brown sweet stuff. It did cause problems when, debonair and meaningful, I tried to sing the latest Elvis song under my breath. You try singing *It's Now or Never* when your teeth are glued together by caramel toffee.

The seats on these old trams were hard and not very wide, and tight trousers made sitting a bit of a pain. My waist seemed to have expanded by an inch or two in the last few weeks. Donna being a well-built girl, her hips took up at least two-thirds of the space, leaving my right buttock uneasily overhanging the aisle and earning me a series of dunts as other couples pushed past. We had to be tightly squeezed together to avoid me

129

falling off as the tram jerked and shoogled its way through the freezing night.

It was quite comforting to be squashed against Donna, although she was wearing one of those starchy petticoats girls used to have, yards and yards of stiff material that made the lower half of her dress stick out like a ripe lettuce, ballooning over my lap. It was difficult to tell exactly where she was inside it.

I laid my arm along the back of the seat, imagining it was round her in an affectionate embrace.

'Mind ma hair!' she shrieked. The problem was that her hairstyle, expanding backwards in that yellow fog, meant that I couldn't make contact with her shoulders. My arm started to feel numb against the hard top edge of the seat. I wiggled my fingers to get some feeling back.

Something was crawling up my arm; a feathery sort of insect. With relief I realised it was the missing strip of eyelashes, stuck to my sleeve. I picked it off and pushed it discreetly into my pocket.

For the rest of the journey we said nothing. It wasn't meaningful silence, just nothing, just silence. It was fine. It left me in peace.

At the terminus, we tottered downstairs and out into the frosty night. Donna started walking and I scampered after, checking my watch.

Twenty minutes till the last tram.

She lived in a bungalow near the tram stop. Handy, I thought, for me to get away afterwards. As we turned through the gate, the front door opened and a little billiard ball head poked out.

'Home at last, Donna,' it squeaked. She paid no attention, just walked past it and into the house. The billiard ball looked at me dubiously. I gave my twisted grin and followed her. There I was, standing at the door of her living-room. It wasn't what I'd intended but there I was.

The whole family was sitting there, round a low table sprouting beer bottles, empty glasses with frothy rims and plates with stained paper doilies on them. A cake covered in frothy pink icing, with a few drunken-looking candles on it, sat in the centre, a few wedges missing. It seemed to be some sort of birthday party.

A man, who must have been Dad, lay sprawled in an armchair, patting at his belly where it tried to burst the tormented buttons of his shirt. A very old woman, Donna's Gran I supposed, sat on an upright chair beside the blazing coal fire, polishing at something with a handkerchief. A woman who looked like Donna but older, probably her Mum, stood over them, hooting. Just like an owl.

'Hoo, hoo, hoo,' she said, in a high-pitched, girlish sort of voice. One or two other people were standing about with glasses in their hands, talking. Another woman, with hair like a wet sheep, was playing on a piano in the corner. *Tum-ti-tum-ti-tum-ti-tum*. The billiard ball went over to her and started singing in a high-pitched wobbly voice, some ancient song about saaailing arooound the world with somebody. The air was sweaty, hotter than the dance hall.

With a shudder I realised that what Gran was polishing was her own upper set of teeth, like peppermint drops on a pink plate. Her top lip looked as if it was being sucked down her throat.

'Hoo hoo hoo,' said Mum.

Dad bumped down his glass of beer, spilling it a bit on the table, and waved at me.

'Come on in,' he said. 'You must be that Ricky Moran Donna is always talking about.'

'Eh ... no.' I said. I looked for Donna to help me, but she just turned away and patted her hair in a mirror. She probably didn't know my name anyway.

'Well, if you're not Moran, who the hell are you, then?'

I wasn't going to tell them my name. The sooner I was out of that room the better. I don't know why I said what I did, but it just slipped out.

'Elvis,' I said. Silence. Incredulous looks all round. The piano gave a single startled *plong*.

Mum gasped, eyes popping. 'You're never Elvis!' she said. 'You're not ... good-looking enough.'

That hurt.

'My mum was a big fan.' I said it too quickly. It was a blunder; I could see them calculating. I knew Elvis was only four years and ninety-eight days older than me.

Dad sorted it. 'Well,' he said, 'I don't care who you are. Give us a song!' And he waved towards the piano. The old sheep started playing again. *Tum-ti-tum-ti-tum*.

This wasn't what I'd come all the way on that tram for. And it got worse. As I turned toward the piano, wondering how I was going to escape from all this, I felt a sudden relaxation round my waist. You know the feeling, a mixture of release and panic. The top button at the front of my trousers, which I had noticed earlier was a bit loose on its thread, had popped right off as I twisted. I grabbed my waist with both hands and felt my eyes widen. Everybody stared at me with interest, thinking I was going to be sick.

131

'Sorry,' I said, straightening my tie and brushing down my lapels with my left hand while the right held the front of my trousers. 'Got to be going. Taxi's waiting. Nice to have met you all.' They looked at me, wondering who I really was. I managed to catch Donna's eye and flicked mine meaningfully at the door. I took her fairly firmly by the arm.

Gran put her teeth back in and smiled at me. That was it. I pulled Donna out of the living room. I didn't want to say goodbye at the door in case the billiard ball popped out again, so we didn't stop till the pavement.

I wasn't going home without a goodnight kiss. Looking solemnly into her lashless eyes, I lifted my chin, trying to reach her face. That much I'd earned. I managed to manoeuvre things so that I was standing on the kerb and Donna was in the gutter. That gave me a few more inches.

I stood on tiptoe. It was just enough.

Our cold lips met.

With a smacking grunt she squeezed me to her. I could feel her mouth sliding across my face.

It was hard to breathe with Donna chomping away. She was strong, too; my feet didn't quite leave the ground, but it was a close thing, especially as I was still having difficulty holding up my trousers. It's not easy, kissing a girl with your hands in your pockets. When she eventually put me down, though, I managed a blissful gasp and stepped back one pace, trying to smooth my hair back into place. Our frozen breath hung in the air around us.

'Well,' I said. 'It's been nice.' Silence. Not much of a talker, was Donna. She looked a bit crazy with lipstick smudged across her face.

There was one duty left. I took a deep breath, relaxed so much my lips almost dropped off my face, made my eyes into slits, and said, out of the side of my mouth, 'See you again?'

I held my breath.

Donna looked me over, taking in my sculpted quiff, my slim tie, my exquisitely painful but now sagging trousers. Her chewing gum shifted from left to right. She had decided.

'Nah,' she said.

Well, that was a surprise. And a relief. I tried to look disappointed. She wobbled back up the garden path. At the door she turned for a last look.

'Elvis!' she muttered. The door slammed.

With as much dignity as I could manage, I walked away, whistling, hands still in my pockets, supporting my trousers. The fingers found the shred of eyelashes. With a shrill blast I tossed it high into the misty darkness. Like a black snowflake, it trembled down to the top of Donna's garden hedge, where it lay, fluttering at me.

And what did it see? It saw me slip on the icy pavement and crash into the gutter, dishevelling my hairstyle and scraping a painful hole in the left knee of my trousers. It hurts, falling with your hands in your pockets.

I scrambled to my feet, just in time to see the last tram rattle into the foggy distance. There was no chance of catching it.

But I was happy. Everyone at the dance knew I had left with Donna; it would be the main topic for Charlie and the others on Monday morning. And that, of course, was what mattered. They didn't know the rest. I wiped the lipstick off my nose.

Shivering in my thin jacket, I limped off on the long, long walk home.

Moore's Alley

A trellis separated the back of Elizabeth's house from the servants' quarters. Sometimes when it rained, for something to do, Elizabeth stood under the eaves outside the kitchen door to look at the thorny branches of bougainvillea that climbed the crisscrossed slats of wood, tangled with purple petals and bright wet leaves.

On the other side of the trellis, a stand of banana trees formed a privacy wall between the garden at the back of the property and the alley. Sometimes, for something to do, Elizabeth sat on the ground in the cool shade of the tunnel-like space between the papery trunks of the trees and the wall of purple sugarcane stalks that faced the alley as if it were a secret room like the one the older girls made with their towels at the pool beneath the diving board. Sometimes crawling out from under the canopy of sharp-edged leaves that bent with their weight to the ground, her arms bumped into the stalks, and the fine dense hairs at the base of the new green shoots stuck to her skin like splinters of glass.

Other times, for something to do, she stood at the corner of the alley, her hand wrapped around the rusty shaft of the signpost there and leaned to the side, turning one way and then the other until flakes of yellow paint and fragments of metal, broke off in the palm of her hand. Sometimes they cut her. And sometimes, like the sugarcane splinters that left stinging welts inside her wrists, sometimes she thought of them as a form of punishment for the things she sometimes did.

Once she was waiting for Romi the maid to open the gate. And, though it was clear from the sound of water pouring onto the floor of the servants' washroom that Romi was bathing, Elizabeth needed her to open the gate. She wasn't sure why she did what she did. Maybe it was because she had decided that what she needed should be Romi's priority. Maybe it was because she knew that she could and no one would do anything about it, but she leaned to the ground for a handful of gravel and hurled it through a small grated opening in the cinderblock wall.

The signpost on the corner read Gang Prajen, but no one called it that. The alley was known as Moore's Alley, the surname of the family who lived at the end of the block. There were three Moore brothers, but everyone knew when anyone said Moore's Alley, they were thinking of the middle brother, Johnnie. Elizabeth thought of him as an extension of his gold racing bike. Sometimes from her hiding place beneath the canopy of sugar cane leaves she watched him come flying out of the alley, his shoulder leaning into the corner, his fingers fastened to the gold tape wrapped around the handle grips that curled down and around like the shell of a snail. Sometimes, balanced for a moment, chest parallel to the bar, rear end cocked above the seat, he looked at her crouched behind the purple stalks before he disappeared around the corner.

Twirling slowly round the pole, Elizabeth stared across the street at the long stretch of mown lawn they called the empty field. Occasionally, someone's father was there with a basket of golf balls and a few clubs, practicing drives. Sometimes on the weekend, the American kids gathered to play capture the flag. Once in a while, a few Indonesian boys came to fly their handmade kites.

Elizabeth's thoughts ran together. The blue and green cellophane kites flying over the field, the long tails, glittering with glass-coated string mixed up with Johnnie on his ten-speed, patting the gold bar between his legs, inviting her to go for a ride.

The creak of a handbrake startled her awake. But it wasn't Johnnie; it was the tukang roti, an old woman pedaling a three-wheeled bicycle attached to the rear of a large wooden crate. 'Roti,' she called out in Indonesian. 'Roti panas dijual.' Hot bread for sale.

Elizabeth shook her head no, thinking the woman was speaking to her, but she continued to sing, 'Roti panas. Roti panas dijual,' which was when Elizabeth turned to see Bruce, the oldest Moore boy, approaching from the other end of the alley.

A metal box lined the inside of the crate to insulate the bread, loaded into the cart, hot from the oven. The woman lifted the hinged lid, and the warm smell of yeast rose in the air. She used tongs to hand him a loaf. Bruce gave her a few Rupiah notes and took a bite.

Elizabeth looked from the bread woman, folding the money inside her brassiere to Bruce's turned back walking down the alley toward his house. His hair was very blonde, very soft. She hadn't forgotten the time at the pool he let her ride his back underwater in the rain, then touched her between the legs and swam away as if he hadn't. More than a year had passed. They hadn't spoken of it since.

135

Without exactly addressing her, he called over his shoulder, 'Aren't you coming over?'

Elizabeth looked behind her, thinking he must be speaking to someone else. 'Coming over?'

'I hear you and Stevie like to play together these days.'

'He's in my class at school.'

'Come over,' he said, taking another bite of the bread. His face was a smooth, quiet brown. His eyes, very light, very clear.

Elizabeth followed Bruce through his back gate. They entered the house through the kitchen. The door made a vacuum hiss as it closed and a wall of air conditioned air hit her in the face. Inside, Mrs. Moore was leaned over at the waist, her head inside the deep freezer. Elizabeth stared at her brown toes gripping the linoleum floor. Her hips were narrow as a girl's in a lean pair of pedal pushers and, when she turned around, her blue-black eyes, were the same blue-black of the star sapphire studs in her ears.

Mrs. Moore handed Bruce a Tupperware container, filled, Elizabeth saw, when he pried off the lid, with frozen Coke. 'Take one to Steven,' Mrs. Moore instructed Elizabeth. 'And spoons.' She pointed to the silverware drawer and leaned inside the freezer again. Elizabeth stared at her very brown ankles, at the backs of her very brown heels.

The Moores gave parties. Unusual parties. Mr. Moore invited the Indonesian engineers who worked in his department. Other Indonesians from the kampung across the river were invited to perform. Men walked barefoot across beds of embers, lit for this purpose on the Moore's front lawn. When the coals flared, they scooped what looked like pools of fire into their bare hands and juggled the flames on the wavy-shaped blades of the sword-length knives called a kris.

Later a band of women floated out of the dark from an opening in the foliage, dressed in tightly wound sarongs, threaded with gold. A heavier length of fabric was wrapped, mid-hip to waistline, and, above this, a long-sleeved, transparent shirt called a baju under which a lace brassiere and a window of skin could be seen. Lifting and turning their bare feet and ankles, the women seemed to climb inside out of themselves as they performed a dance that involved balancing china plates on the palms of their hands while turning their bare wrists and long fingers in circles above their heads, behind their backs, and under their knees.

Children were invited to the Moore's parties, and for a few hours were allowed like the three brothers to run wild, unattended and unaccounted for behind the closed doors of the boys' bedrooms; in the screened-in servants' quarters; outside with the Indonesian performers. Some wandered farther away, out the kitchen door and down the alley to the playground behind the American school where they climbed the fence and mounted the staircase to the roof above the tennis courts. Here they smoked the cigarettes they'd bought from the cigarette man or stolen from their fathers' bureau drawers and exchanged stories about who among the parents and which of the servants or teachers or nurses and sometimes even the sailors from the tankers were secretly involved with one another and where they went and what they did and when and how they knew.

'Kupu-kupu malam,' someone said. 'They're butterflies of the night. Even the fathers are butterflies at night.' Then someone would point to a moth banging its wings against the street light and change the subject.

When he wasn't working for the company as a mechanical engineer, Mr. Moore was a hunter. Sometimes he travelled by jeep to central Sumatra with a Chinese-Indonesian by the name of Mr. Tow where they hunted wild boar and sometimes tigers. Once at a party, Mr. Moore showed an eight millimeter filmstrip of one of the kills and, beneath the torch-lit front lawn, unfurled the skin of a tiger, the head still attached. The children touched the small scars in the terrier-rough coat of the face, and then the glass eyes, the bared teeth.

For a while the boys kept a pet tiger their father had brought home from a hunt. When Mr. Tow realized the carcass was a lactating female, he searched the path leading into the jungle until he found the cub in a stand of trees. They stowed it in a gunny sack in the back of the jeep, and Mr. Moore took it home to his sons. It was only a few months old. The size of a small dog. They put a collar around its neck and attached it by a long chain to the legs of a picnic table on the patio behind the porch. During the day it liked to wander through the waist-high elephant ear leaves in the garden. At night it slept in Steven's bed.

Stevie and Elizabeth sat on the floor in his room.

'What was his name?' Elizabeth asked, scraping her spoon across the top of the frozen brown foam.

'Who?'

'Your tiger.'

'She. Her name was Lucy.'

'Lucy? Why Lucy?'

'I don't know. It was John's idea.'

'How did she sleep exactly, when she slept with you?'

'With her head on my pillow. Her back pressed into my chest. She had this growl when she breathed. Have you ever slept with a cat?'

'I can't. I'm allergic.'

'Her growl was deeper than the sound a cat makes. The vibration was stronger. I could feel it in my chest through her coat. Sometimes I used to lie awake just to listen to her breathe. Sometimes it felt better than sleep.'

'She never scratched you?'

Stevie shook his head no. 'Sometimes she liked to lick me. You probably don't know this if you've never had a cat. Their tongues are like sandpaper. Rough, but a little bit wet. And warm. Kind of like a squeezed out wash rag, but scratchy. It feels strange at first. Then you get used to it. I've heard a shark's skin feels like that.'

'Where did she lick you?'

'Anywhere. The side of my face. Sometimes she curled down under the covers. Sometimes she licked my stomach.'

Elizabeth stared at Stevie's lowered eyes and watched him thinking of Lucy.

'Are you coming over today?' she asked.

'I don't know. Later. You go first. I don't like Bruce to tease me.'

'But you're coming, right? I don't want to set everything up if you're not coming.'

'I'm coming.'

Bruce was lying on top of his bedspread reading a paperback when Elizabeth passed the door of his bedroom. 'Finished so soon?'

Elizabeth left the way she came through the kitchen door. As she crossed the patio, she glanced at the picnic table pushed against the wall, a rusty chain wrapped in a tangle around one of the legs and a small bowl turned upside down on the concrete. There was a bare spot of ground at the edge of the patio where the grass had stopped growing.

No one talked about it, but everyone knew. One day the tiger cub had climbed on top of the picnic table, and, leaping to the bench after a butterfly or a lizard, had fallen off without enough chain. One of the servants found her. Mr. Moore was called home from the office and rough-tongued Lucy with the trembling purr that made Stevie feel more protected than sleep had been taken away, no one knew where, while the boys were still at school.

138

Their second Christmas in Sungai Gerong, Elizabeth's mother had ordered a set of patio furniture constructed of woven rattan for the new house. As an afterthought, she asked the furniture maker to build a doll-sized set of furniture for Elizabeth's family of Barbie dolls. She had them all, the old one with the black pony tail, the new one with the blonde flip, the Ken doll, the younger sister Skipper, the boyfriend Scooter.

In a corner of her bedroom, Elizabeth had pushed two card tables together and draped a spare bedspread over them. Underneath, it was as if she were inside a house without windows. A house without a door. One night she connected a reading lamp to an extension cord, dragged it inside, and draped a red chiffon scarf she had taken from her mother's drawer over the shade. The room looked on fire.

The doll-sized bamboo chairs were arranged around a miniature table at the center of the make-believe room. The armoire, was decked with a thimble, the silver coin Luardia had given her, a pearl earring without a back, and a miniature silver rickshaw with a bent wheel that had broken off of her charm bracelet. The two rattan beds Elizabeth draped with white linen napkins and arranged perpendicularly on either side of a table leg at the corner, thinking the dolls could talk to each other better that way, lying head to head.

Elizabeth wasn't supposed to close her bedroom door when she had guests but, today, no one but the servants were home. The small knock at the door was Romi, the maid.

'Silakan masuk,' Elizabeth said and lifted the edge of the bedspread that grazed the floor. The door opened just wide enough for her to see Romi's smooth brown toes beside the calloused edges of Stevie's feet. The bedroom door closed and Stevie crawled beneath the bedspread. He sat where he always sat beside the beds in the room within the room.

Whether a day had gone by or several weeks, the play began where they left off. Elizabeth lifted one of the dolls out of the storage box and introduced her with a name and a description of her characteristics that she made up on the spot.

I'm Jinx. I look just like Karen Watson, except I have long blonde hair. Really long hair. It reaches all the way to my waist. And I have long straight bangs too. They're always in my eyes.

Stevie slid to the floor, his weight on one elbow, the side of his face propped in his hand. The old Barbie with the black ponytail was dressed in a black and silver evening dress. He lifted her out of the box and, with

139

his stubby fingers, reached beneath the skirt of the dress so that he could make her feet walk across the floor. He held her by the top of her head and twirled her around.

Look, Jinx. See how my skirt billows around my legs? Isn't it pretty?

I suppose. I don't really care much about dresses. Let's go for a ride on my motorcycle. We can look for the moon.

Stevie lifted the doll's arms over her head. *I feel so sleepy. I've been dancing for hours, and I've had so much to drink. Let's go to bed.*

'Wait,' Elizabeth said to Stevie. 'You haven't said what your doll's name is.'

'It's Quentin.'

'Quentin? Do you mean like Morley Quentin? That's a boy's name.'

'It doesn't matter. It can be a girl's name if I want it to be. My name can be a girl's name. Haven't you ever known a girl named Stevie?'

'No, but my mother has a girlfriend named Johnnie.'

'See? *Now, let's go to bed. But, Jinx, do you think you could help me with my zipper first?*

Of course. Turn around, Quentin.

Stevie turned the doll so that her back faced the doll Elizabeth held by the waist. He slipped the sleeveless gown off of her shoulders and over her hips and lifted the doll out of the dress.

Turn around, Jinx. I'll undo your zipper now.

I'm not wearing a dress. I'm wearing capris. Can't you see? They're the kind your mother wears. See? I have a side zipper. I can undo it myself.

All right. I'll wait for you in my bed.

Stevie tucked the undressed doll beneath the linen napkin.

Elizabeth pulled off the trousers and pulled off the blouse and flounced the doll around the top of the table. *I did so want to go look for the moon,* she had Jinx say. *I'll never be able to fall asleep now.*

I have an idea, Stevie had Quentin say. *Have you ever gone invisible swimming?*

Invisible swimming? What's that?

You do it with your eyes closed. I'll show you.

Ok. Elizabeth pranced the undressed doll on top of the table, then made her hop to the floor and walked her to the bed situated perpendicular to the bed where Stevie had put his doll.

Let's whisper, Stevie's doll Quentin said to Elizabeth's doll Jinx.

I can't hear you, Elizabeth said.

Come into my bed, then, Stevie made Quentin say.

140

The two dolls lay side by side beneath the linen napkin Elizabeth had unfolded.

'Should I trade her for the Ken doll?' Elizabeth asked.

'Let's try it like this,' Stevie said and turned the two dolls on their sides.

Don't you think it's hot tonight? Stevie had Quentin say. *I think the air conditioner must be broken. Let's kick off the covers.* He lay the two dolls on top of the napkin and with a kick of Quentin's foot, pushed the napkin to the floor. He placed Quentin on top of Jinx, so that they were lying face to face, hip to hip. Stevie held the Quentin doll by the hips. *Shall I show you how to go invisible swimming now?* Stevie had Quentin ask.

Elizabeth didn't answer and wondered if Bruce had told Stevie about the time he had touched her between the legs at the pool.

Stevie turned the Quentin doll on her back and rotated the Jinx doll around so that her face lay between Quentin's legs and her pelvis rested on Quentin's face.

Elizabeth watched, from where she was lying on the floor, her chin propped on her fist. Stevie slid his hand inside his shorts. Elizabeth waited.

Do to me what I do to you, Stevie had Quentin say to Jinx. *Ok?*

Unable to speak, Elizabeth nodded her head.

With his other hand, Stevie rubbed the Jinx doll's face between Quentin's legs. Then he lifted and dropped her hips in soft beats against the Quentin doll's face.

Stevie's eyes were closed. He had let go of the dolls and was breathing from his mouth. When he opened his eyes, he smiled. 'That's how you go invisible swimming.'

'How did you know?'

'That's what my brother does with Karen Watson when they play Truth or Consequences. Sometimes he lets me watch.'

'Does she know?'

'Know what?'

'That you're watching.'

Stevie shrugged.

'What do you think it tastes like?' Elizabeth asked, but a knock on glass distracted them. Elizabeth ducked her head under the hem of the bedspread that covered the card table. The sun was bright in the row of windows that crossed the wall, squares of glass beneath the ceiling. Idi the cook was standing on a ladder, doing something, it seemed, to the air conditioner, but his eye scanned the room and held Elizabeth's gaze when they met.

Elizabeth returned the dolls to the box and folded the linen napkins over the doll-sized bamboo beds. She crawled out from under the table and pulled the bedspread to the floor where she left it in a heap for Romi to fold. Stevie followed, tugging at the hem of his shorts and straightening the pockets.

'Do you want something to drink?' Elizabeth asked.

Stevie shook his head no. 'I have to go now.'

Elizabeth walked him to the kitchen door and outside as far as the gate, where Idi was squatted now beside the oil drum where the trash was burned in the alley. He was using a machete to cut six-foot stalks of sugarcane into shorter lengths. He held the edge of the blade to the purple husk that was dense and tough as bamboo and used the heel of his palm to push the blade down the stalk until the husk was peeled away from the white fiber inside. He cut the skinned stalk in two, and handed one piece to Elizabeth and one to Stevie. 'Tebu,' he said.

Stevie bit down on the stalk and gnawed on it until the juice filled his mouth. 'Air tebu,' he said to Idi. 'Sugarcane water,' he said to Elizabeth. 'You don't eat it. You suck the juice out.' He swallowed the juice and spit the chewed fiber to the ground. 'I have to go now,' he said to Elizabeth. Terima kasih,' he said to Idi.

Elizabeth watched him leave. The back of his neck was a smooth, quiet brown like his brothers', but he was chubbier than they were, and something about the way he sort of skipped when he walked looked girlish.

Elizabeth gnawed on her stalk, glancing now and again at the teeth marks left in what looked like a stick of wet white wood. She was thinking about the taste of the sugarcane water pooled in her mouth. It wasn't sugar water sweet. It was a cleaner taste than that, like Stevie's eyes. And she wondered why the one thing made her think of the other.

The sugarcane water tasted like the water inside the coconuts that, on other days, Idi sometimes cut open for her, squatted beside the oil drum where he was squatted now. She looked at his hands skinning the purple stalks of cane and thought of the way he pulled the green husk away from the hard brown shell of the nut that he gripped in the blade of the machete and tapped on the asphalt until it split open like a skull. He would hand her one of the halves filled with the coconut water to drink, then use the tip of the machete to pry the soft white meat away from the shell. He always held the blade close to her mouth, but she had never once tried to eat from it the way his children did. She lifted the coconut meat off the blade with her fingers.

Remembering the taste, she thought of the word manis, the Indonesian word for sweet, and how different sweet tasted in Indonesian. Like the sugarcane water she'd swallowed. Like a girl she once knew. Someone sweet, someone lost. Like the fiber she'd spit to the ground.

DAVID SWANN

Drought

In hills north of the famous resort, we slip stiles beyond the dam, looking for signs.

The tourists must be thirsty in their boarding-houses. They've left black lines around the valley's basin. The reservoir is dwindling, its mud cracked.

Miles away, they'll be rinsing sand from their kids' feet, comparing the heat to Spain. But here, save for the fruit-machine twitter of sparrows, it's quiet. A breeze off the moors. Ghosts in the wires.

My mother and I pause on a fallen wall under the shadow of a tree, watching wading-birds, busy as librarians in their aisles. Ahead is an island that's maybe the hill my grandfather sledged as a child.

She isn't sure. So much has changed since they evacuated the villagers and flooded their valley. An old tale: the few make way for the many. Only the bridge gained pardon. She points out its arch, a whale rising – before turning away to study a tree loaded with damsons.

Then she says it, with a child's wonder: 'I see it now. This is my Grandma's garden.'

There are sunken places, so the tales say – from which the dead call, and bells churn in storms. But the planners were cunning here, left no spires piercing the lake, only a few flattened barns and these straggling walls.

We sit on as the fruit darkens over our heads, and the shadows creep out.

They're stretched now, and thin. We watch them go down where they must, from the ruins to the water.

KAREN SMYTE

Dentures

The true last night of our father, I curled around my little brother and his heavy sleep-breathing, his skin offering a faint sweet water funk from an evening swim. A worrisome pause between his inhale and exhale kept me up. I covered Pete's ears when our dad said he was leaving for good.

'Your father's gone,' mom told us in the morning. 'It's hard for a man to see his wife with no teeth.' The first dentist she ever visited, after she had me, took all her teeth, said the pregnancy had done that. She didn't ask for a second opinion. 'An old lady, not even 30. He wants to think he's young. I don't need that.'

We suspended our game of hide-mom's-dentures, resisted playing with the false teeth that bathed each night in a clear glass on top her bedside table. Our father left because he was a leaver, it's what he knew how to do. This time, though, he left his wedding band.

'Aren't you glad you were with him and had us?' I said, to cheer her up. To cheer us up.

'I would have had children with someone else.' She took a drag on her cigarette, held it in her throat, made an 'O' shape with her mouth and released first a thick, slow-moving smoke ring, then a small, quick one that joined the other in the air.

'But you wouldn't have had us. And you love us.'

'I would have loved other children too, honey.'

RACHEL ROBB

467 Strathmore Ave.

Over there is the house of the young woman who died on the corner of Gerrard and Woodfield when a pickup truck jumped the curb last summer.

The stop sign became a makeshift memorial – indignant coronations and hand written notes of loss pinned to the wooden pole. Then the flowers began to sag and words bled across paper like inky tributaries. A steely Samaritan cleared it all up one night. A quiet act of compassion.

She knew her only from a courteous distance. For example, she remembers her sinewy neck as she dug a shallow flowerbed last spring. Soily kneecaps peeking out, childlike, from denim cutoffs.

'Nick, it's been a year.'

Spoken, surreptitiously, from behind a newspaper, as the teenage daughter, darker and less sinewy, demands her phone back.

She was with her two whippets and one of them survived the wreck in that strange twist of luck certain animals possess. She sees him on the porch standing sentinel while his now single parent empties the recycling bin.

Now, the daughter refuses a ride to school and walks north before disappearing – stubbornly, heartbreakingly – into the day.

Finally, she knows he's just a dog but he looks as mournful as a grieving person some mornings. His tiny shivery jumps when a car reverses unexpectedly are a stubborn reminder of how unsettled they all felt in the days after she was hit and how quickly, with such shameful relief, they stopped talking about the accident and returned to their own private calamities.

CHRISTINA EAGLES

Thinning the Crop

When Susan's husband was made redundant, leaving them with three small children and no way to pay the mortgage, she talked about how our father used to thin his apples. Every June, he balanced on a step-ladder, reached up into the tree and broke off the discards, dropping them for Susan and me to collect. We gathered the hard, green balls in seaside pails and used them to play lopsided marbles.

Susan's husband ranted. The company had been out to get him. But Susan told him no. It wasn't personal. They had only done what our father did for the apples. Too heavy a crop could have broken the branch. It had to be done.

Six months later, I collect her from the clinic. I have brought a box of tissues and rehearsed a mouthful of platitudes. But Susan is calm, as if what she has done was no more than removing a wisdom tooth.

When we reach the car, I open my arms to her, but she shakes her head, dry-eyed.

'Dad would have understood,' she says. 'I've only thinned the crop so that the others can grow strong.'

What lies did the apple tree murmur to console itself, as our father worked along its branches and those small, green not yet apples bounced at its feet?

Cure

The angel in the bathroom didn't want a conversation. She gave her instructions then turned away, stroking my face with thick, black wings.

'Don't you want it hot?' I said, leaning against the towel rail as she ran the bath. Flies buzzed against the window – some fighting to get in, others fighting to get out.

'I miss the cold.' She handed me her sword and I propped it in the corner next to the lavatory brush. The blade was gold, like her eyes, but tarnished, like the scales on her cheeks.

She switched on the radio and I tapped my lips with a finger. 'My son is asleep.' Nodding, she turned the volume down low. When the bath was full, she slipped beneath the water and watched me as bubbles escaped her lips.

'Does it help the pain?' I asked.

A nod. A blink. A smile. Darkness billowed from her skin, inking the bathwater and staining the enamel. Wind bucked the windowpane as the water began to boil. Fingers of vapour curled towards me as the surface foamed and hissed.

Her voice came to me through the steam. 'Now!'

The sword was heavier than before and I struggled to place the tip against her breast. It took all my strength to slide the blade between her ribs. When her body had melted, I woke my son, put him in his chair and wheeled him through. I undressed him and sat on the bathroom floor, waiting for the water to cool.

CAROLYN PRIOR

Watford Gap services

There is a bridge. It crosses to the other side, a conduit for staff and stock, relic of older times. Skeletal iron aged to a colour that evokes neither paint nor rust spans the rushing metal blockade between north and south. A woman sits at a picnic table watching the steps that twist down from the mesh walkway. Around her people smoke, hunched collars, spare hands in pockets. She's not a smoker, ignores the ashtray on her table, swills a chilling coffee round its cardboard cup as she checks her phone again, continues her observation of the bridge.

Her head lifts. She swings one leg over the awkward bench, hesitates, waits. A man and a boy are walking slowly over the bridge. Hand in hand they stop to watch a large lorry, turning from one barrier to the other to point and follow. They are laughing, shouting against the turbulence.

A stumbling hop to extricate her other leg, then she's crossing the car park. The boy runs down the steps and nestles into her. Heavy feet on the metal stamp her tender face closed. She straightens as he thrusts a hand towards her, takes the backpack, the boy soft against her thigh. He speaks, she counters, the boy stiffening as they spit a mist of bile that drizzles over his head.

The man crouches, knots his arms tight round the quiet boy. She waits. He stands, turns away from them, starts back across the bridge.

Biographies

Judges

Patience Agbabi was born in London to parents from Nigeria and grew up in Wales. One of the UK's foremost poets, she studied English Language and Literature at Pembroke College, Oxford University, and is a former Poet Laureate of Canterbury. Her writing and performance has been featured on radio and TV worldwide. In 2015 she was a recipient of The Cholmondeley Award and shortlisted for the Ted Hughes Prize for New Work in Poetry. Patience is the author of four books, *R.A.W, Transformatrix, Bloodshot Monochrome* and *Telling Tales* (Canongate, 2014). *Telling Tales* is a retelling of Chaucer's The Canterbury Tales for the 21st century. Mining the Middle-English masterwork for its performance as well as its poetry and pilgrims, her boisterous and lyrical collection gives one of Britain's most significant works of poetry thrilling new life. Following a book launch at Southwark Cathedral, Patience has toured the book with literature producers Renaissance One to a range of literary festivals and venues. She lives in Kent.

Tessa Hadley has written six novels including *The London Train, Clever Girl* and *The Past*, and two collections of short stories. She publishes stories regularly in the *New Yorker*, reviews for the *London Review of Books* and the *Guardian*, and is a Professor at Bath Spa University.

Tim Stevenson was the winner of the 2013 National Flash-Fiction Day 100-Word competition and has been published in the anthologies *Jawbreakers, Scraps, Eating My Words, Landmarks, Guided By Surprise and War, Conflict and Resolution* as well as in *Synaesthesia Magazine, The List Magazine* and online at 1000Words amongst others. His collection of flash-fiction *The Book Of Small Changes* was published in 2014, and a short story collection *On Cleanliness and Other Things* was published in 2015. He lives near Winchester.

Karen Ashe was brought up in Airdrie and now lives in Glasgow with her family. 'Rebound', the first short story she ever wrote took second place in the *South China Morning Post* short story competition, and she went on to complete the MLitt in Creative Writing at Glasgow University. She now spends Monday evenings in the inspiring company of Chryston Writer's Group. As well as short stories, she also writes poetry, recently placing third in the FWS Easter poetry competition, and making the shortlist for the Glasgow Women's Library Short Story competition. She writes flash fiction and has been published online in Paragraph Planet. Karen is one of Scottish Book Trust New Writers Awardees for 2016. She has been shortlisted for the Fish Short Story, Flash Fiction and Poetry prizes, the Bridport Prize for Flash Fiction. 'Never on a Friday' was published in the Mslexia Curious Incidents section, and more recently, 'The Bearded Lady', in their Monster-themed New Writing showcase.

Jennifer Bailey grew up in Lancashire and gradually travelled south, via Manchester, Nottingham and Leicester, to London. During that time, she taught at a series of universities that included Leicester, Nottingham, California State University in Sacramento and London's City University. She has written literary fiction throughout her academic career, and with some publishing success in recent years writing now takes priority.

Sarah Barr writes about relationships, the natural world, loss and hope. She teaches creative writing in Dorset and for the Open University, gives readings and runs writing workshops. Her poetry and short stories have been published in various magazines and anthologies including, *Meniscus*, *The Frogmore Papers*, *South*, *The Interpreter's House*. She has completed her first (as yet unpublished) novel. Her poem, 'January', won the Frogmore Poetry Prize 2015. She was a Bridport Prize winner in 2010 with her poem, 'Clearing the Ice'.

Wendy Brandmark is a novelist and short story writer. Her collection of short stories, *He Runs the Moon: Tales from the Cities*, was published by Holland Park Press in 2016. Her last novel, *The Stray American* (Holland Park Press, 2014), about an American lawyer adrift in London, was longlisted for the Jerwood Fiction Uncovered Prize 2015. Her first novel, *The Angry Gods* (Dewi Lewis Publishing), explored racism and difference in New York City in the 1950s and 1970s. Her short stories have appeared widely in anthologies and journals, including *North American Review*,

Riptide Journal, *The Massachusetts Review*, *Stand Magazine* and *The Warwick Review*. She has been a recipient of an Arts Council award towards the writing of short stories. She has been a fellow at the Virginia Centre for the Creative Arts, and had residencies at the Tyrone Guthrie Centre in Ireland. Her fiction reviews have appeared in a range of magazines and newspapers, including *The Times Literary Supplement*, *The Literary Review* and *The Independent*. She teaches fiction writing at The City Lit and supervises students on the Oxford University MSt in Creative Writing. She grew up in New York City but now lives in London. She is currently working on both short stories and a new novel. http://wendybrandmark.com

Glynis Charlton writes poetry, short stories and unidentified pieces of fiction. Always drawn to the bleak and unsettling, she is currently finishing her first psychological crime novel. Her poems have appeared in a number of anthologies, including the *Grist Anthology of New Writing*. She has also scripted a film short that was screened at Leeds Film Festival, and a digital short shown on the BBC. Glynis gave up the day job in 2002 and has worked as an arts freelancer ever since. When not writing or walking on Haworth moor, she runs workshops across Yorkshire, leads a writing retreat in Italy and works at various festivals. www.glynischarlton.com

Jenny Danes was born in Chelmsford in 1995 and studies at Newcastle University. In 2013 she was highly commended in the Bridport Prize for poetry and in 2016 she won The Poetry Business New Poets Prize. Her work has appeared in various magazines including The North, Magma and Brittle Star.

Kathleen Donkin lived most of her adult life in New York City where she was in private practice as a psychologist, until she moved to Maine. Prior to receiving her doctorate in psychology she was, at various points, a house-painter, telephone book deliverer, merchant sailor, salvage yard worker, tutor, waitress, night secretary, cold caller, transcriber, and dish washer. The list is not exhaustive. 'Open House' is her first published story.

Christina Eagles is a Scot who has lived in Derbyshire's Peak District for the last thirty years. She has written intermittently for most of that time. In 2014 she was placed third in Fish Flash Fiction award. With semi-retirement from communication skills training she hopes to devote more time to writing and to her other passion, her horse. Her first novel won the David Thomas award for unpublished novels and she is currently seeking an agent for her second.

Elizabeth Ezra is an academic from California who now lives in Scotland and writes books about cinema. She also writes for children, and won the Kelpies Prize in 2016.

Mark Farley was raised in Africa and now lives in Swindon. He writes short stories, flash fiction and the occasional poem. Currently, he's ghost-writing the autobiography of a tree dragon named Crimble. His published work includes: 'Flying Ants', *Flash*: The International Short-Short Story Magazine; 'The Broccoli House', New Realm; 'Hugs are more important than potatoes', Amaryllis Poetry; 'Said the Doctor', 'Spilling Cocoa Over Martin Amis'; 'The Bionic Teeth' and 'The Biology Lesson', Nebula Rift; 'Earlier Than Camels', Domestic Cherry; and 'Grans & Ammo', *Sanitarium Horror Magazine*. Discuss dragons and demons – and attempting to write a million words in a year – with Mark on twitter (@mumbletoes) or via his blog http://mumbletoes.blogspot.com/

Sally Franicevich lives and writes in Auckland, New Zealand. In 2013, her short story 'The Nut Machine' won the Fish Publishing Prize and appeared in that year's *Fish Anthology*. In 2015 her work was long listed for the E.Jolley Prize and was shortlisted in 2014 for the Bridport Prize.

Jeremy Galgut lives in Nottingham. He has had over forty stories published in a range of magazines and anthologies and has won first prizes in the University of Plymouth Short Fiction, New Writer and Brittle Star competitions. Publications his work has appeared in also include *The Edinburgh Review*, *The Middlesex University Press Anthology* and *The Huddersfield University Grist Anthology*. He earns sufficient money to command an average annual writing income of £136.55. Jeremy is also a novelist and a prolifically successful recipient of encouraging rejection letters.

Beatrice Garland lives and works in London, though most of her poems are about the natural world. She has won both the National Poetry Prize (2001) and the Strokestown International Poetry Prize (2002) and published one volume of poetry (*The Invention of Fireworks*, published by Templar Press in 2013), which was short-listed for the Forward Prize for Best First Collection. She is currently at work on a second collection. www.beatricegarland.co.uk

Helena Grey is writer of short stories and flash fiction. She is currently writing a historical novel based on a murder that took place in the Black Country in 1906. Helena has been Commended in the Orwell Society Dystopian Fiction Competition, and winner of a Pre-Raphaelite Society Short Fiction Competition. She is studying an MA in Creative Writing at BCU. Publications include 'The Cradley Tragedy' published in *Lifelines*, and 'Rope and Cliff' published in *Alone Together*, both published by Imprimata.

Jo Holmwood grew up in Devon and has lived in Ireland since 1997. Her work has been shortlisted for the Bristol Short Story Prize, the Fish Publishing Prize and the Mslexia Women's Short Story Competition. In 2013 she published a book of short stories entitled *Under the one roof* as an outcome of a six-month writer-in-residence project at the Bush Hotel, Carrick-on-Shannon. She also writes plays for stage and radio and has directed and produced her own work for audiences in Leitrim, Galway and Dublin. www.arrooabu.com

Ben Johnson is a poet based on the edge of the New Forest, UK. In 2010 his poem 'Pantone 1665 C' won second place in the July IBPC competition. In 2013 he was one of three International winners of the Fermoy Poetry Competition and short-listed for the Bridport Prize. In 2014 his poem 'Selkie' was highly commended in the Bristol Poetry Prize. He has had work published in several print anthologies and online in Antiphon, Ink, Sweat and Tears and RP&D. He is currently the editor for the literary magazine *The Beacon*.

Lesley Krueger is a novelist, short story writer and film maker based in Toronto. Her new novel, *Mad Richard*, will be published in March 2017 in the U.S. and Canada by ECW Press. The book is based on the life of 19th-century British painter Richard Dadd, once the most promising young artist of his generation, later a murderer incarcerated in Bedlam. According to Terry Gilliam, 'The knitting together of Charlotte Brontë's and Richard Dadd's different trajectories works like a dream. I was enthralled.' Related by marriage to Dadd, Lesley drew on family papers for her work. She was also the first runner-up in the 2016 Prism International short fiction contest. The author of six previous books, Lesley lives in Toronto with her husband, and is an enthusiastic member of a women's hockey league.

Anthony Lawrence has published sixteen books of poems and a novel. His most recent collection is *Headwaters* (Pitt Street Poetry, 2016). He teaches Writing Poetry and Creative Writing at Griffith University, Gold Coast, and lives on the far north coast of New South Wales.

Isabella Mead grew up in Cambridge. She holds an MA in History of Art and is currently studying for a degree in French and Spanish. Formerly a secondary English teacher in East London, she worked as a teacher trainer with VSO in a Rwandan village for two years before moving into education departments at The Roald Dahl Museum and Story Centre and The Story Museum in Oxford, where she is currently Head of Learning. www.poemsforathousandhills.wordpress.com

Mark Pajak was born in Merseyside. His work has been highly commended in both the Cheltenham and National Poetry Competitions. He is 2016's Apprentice Poet in Residence at Ilkley Literature Festival and a recipient of a Northern Writers' Award. His first pamphlet has been selected as a Laureate's Choice and will be published by smithldoorstop in late October.

Rizwan Piracha lives and works in South London. He has worked for the NHS since 2003, first as a filing clerk and then, propelled by ruthless ambition and the obsolescence of non-digital means of storing information, as a database clerk. He has also worked night shifts, day shifts and twilight shifts in various warehouses and supermarkets. The twin catalysts for his first attempt at coherent writing were the spiritual enrichment and material impoverishment occasioned by fatherhood. His story 'Lions' made the Bristol prize longlist but his work has not previously been published or read by anyone other than a few ambivalent competition judges.

Caroline Price was born in Middlesex; she studied Music at York University and the Guildhall School of Music and Drama in London, and has worked as a violinist and teacher in Glasgow, London and Kent, where she now lives. She has published three collections of poetry, most recently *Wishbone* (Shoestring Press, 2008), and is preparing a fourth for publication in 2017. Her short stories have appeared in literary magazines including *Stand Magazine, Cyphers* and *The Reader* and have been short-listed in recent years for the Asham Award, the Bridport Prize and the London Magazine Short Story Award. In 2015 she was runner-up for the Society of Authors' Tom-Gallon Award for her short story 'Vin Rouge' (*Something Was There*, anthology of short stories ed. Kate Pullinger, Virago 2011).

Carolyn Prior lives in North Kent and writes Young Adult fiction. She started developing her writing when the children left home, quickly realising that it was much more interesting than her day job in accountancy. 'Watford Gap services' is her first piece to be published.

Rachel Robb is a writer and secondary school teacher from Toronto, Canada. She is a graduate of English and Philosophy from the University of Toronto. She placed 1st in Hamilton's 2014 gritLIT festival for her short collection of poems entitled, *Notes from the First Year*. At present, Rachel is taking a break from teaching to work on a collection of short stories.

Karen Smyte, is a graduate of the Warren Wilson MFA Program, Columbia Journalism School, and Princeton University, and the founder/mentor of Red Beard Press, a youth-driven publishing press based out of Ann Arbor's teen center, The Neutral Zone. Her short story, 'Anya', a chapter from a novel-in-progress, was awarded the 2015 Stella Kupferberg Memorial Prize. She is the recipient of Mesa Refuge and Vermont Studio Residencies and the recipient of a 2016 Barbara Deming Memorial Fund Grant. A former Canadian national team rower, newspaper reporter, and collegiate rowing coach, she now records incarcerated mothers and grandmothers reading bedtime stories to their children and serves as President for Children's Literacy Network.

Eilis Stanley is a poetry and prose writer living in Co. Wicklow, Ireland who has lived in London and San Francisco. She has co-founded and been a member of a number of Poetry Groups over the years (London Women Poetry Group in the 80s); wrote monthly culture and psychology articles for San Francisco Post (1995-2000) and set up Kulture Klub Co.

Wicklow, 2004 with a local fellow poet. She is a member of the well-established Airfield Writers, Dublin since 2008. She won first prize for Short Poem Original at Listowel International Poetry Competition in 2011; was shortlisted for the Bridport poetry Competition in 2012 and at Strokestown International Poetry Competition in 2016. Currently Eilis is working on her first collection and pulling the threads together for a memoir. She is passionate about reviving poetry readings, especially at local community level.

Jean Stevens is a poet and playwright. Her poems have been published in numerous magazines, newspapers and anthologies and broadcast on BBC Radio Three and Four, and she has won the *Yorkshire Post* Poetry Prize and Leeds Libraries Writing Prize. Her plays have been performed at Derby Playhouse, Edinburgh Festival, Harrogate Theatre, Leeds Grand Theatre and West Yorkshire Playhouse. She has also worked as an actor and has numerous credits for stage, screen and radio. She has taught Creative Writing in schools, colleges and top security prisons. Her latest collection of poems is *Beyond Satnav* published by Indigo Dreams Publishing (2016).

David Swann has worked as a tutor of Creative Writing in prisons, schools, homeless centres, universities, and Greek harbour-sides. His short stories and poems have been widely published, including six previous successes in the Bridport Prize and two in the National Poetry Competition. *The Privilege of Rain* (Waterloo Press), based on his experiences as a writer-in-residence in a high-security jail, was shortlisted for The Ted Hughes Award. Born and raised in Accrington, Dave has done a wide range of jobs in the UK and Holland, and is now a Senior Lecturer in English & Creative Writing at the University of Chichester. He agrees with the poet Lawrence Ferlinghetti that literature is the 'shortest distance between two humans'.

Jim Waite was born and educated in Edinburgh in 1942. After teaching English in Campbeltown and Edinburgh, and finally becoming a headteacher in Perth where he still lives, he retired in 2002 to write and travel. His poetry, stories and plays have been published, performed and broadcast. In recent years he has won the Neil Gunn Poetry Prize, the Wigtown Book Festival Scots Poetry Prize and the James McCash Scots Poetry Award. Publication: *My Left Foot Foxtrots – poems in Scots and English* (Comelybank)

Laura Watson lives and writes in Pine, Colorado. She is a graduate of the MFA program at the University of Florida. Her work has appeared in numerous publications including *The Cincinnati Review*, *Poetry Northwest* and *American Poetry Journal*. When not writing poetry, she works as a General Contractor remodeling and building new homes with her husband.

John Wheeler is a familiar face at live poetry venues in and around London including the Poetry Society's *Poetry Café*. He has written and performed for many years and is a multiple poetry 'slam' winner. He was a Farrago UK Finalist and Genesis Finalist in 2015. He lives in Kent and works as a teacher.

Jill Widner is a graduate of the Iowa Writers' Workshop and lives and teaches in Yakima, Washington. She was the recipient of a 2016 MacDowell Colony Fellowship; a Hawthornden Fellowship (Scotland); an Artist Trust/Washington State Arts Commission Fellowship; an Artist Trust Project Grant; and she has been selected for residencies at the Banff Centre; the Corporation of Yaddo; the Virginia Center for the Creative Arts; and VCCA-France. Her fiction has appeared in journals including *Asia Literary Review, American Short Fiction; Everywhere Stories* (Press 53); *The Fiddlehead: Atlantic Canada's International Literary Journal* and *Shenandoah*. Her story 'The Empty Houses' won the 2015 Orison Books anthology award in fiction.